TAKE TWO TABLETS is ι
obesity and hypertension. The auth
Bible and find the roots of preven  *. ...scinating book offers*
*valuable advice on diet, sex, and even depression; it is a comprehensive guide
to healthy living.*

—Professor Talia Miron - Schatz
Director, Institute for the Study of Medical Decision Making
Ono Academic College, Kiryat Ono, Israel

(This book) *is a must read for all women and men, married or single, who
are looking to improve their health and their outlook on life. Drs. Einav,
Kash, and Friedland enlighten their readers with thorough research of how our
forefathers were able to decrease their stress in order to live longer and healthier
in days before modern medicine. This book describes the remarkably simple
changes used by our ancestors that can be easily adapted to modern day life to
improve your quality of life.*

—Dr. Mark H. Einstein, MD, MS
Professor of Obstetrics & Gynecology and Women's Health
Albert Einstein College of Medicine, Bronx, NY

*As the co-founder of the World Academy of Anti-Aging Medicine, I took
great interest in learning how Biblical personalities figuratively or naturally
lived long lives. TAKE TWO TABLETS: Medicine from the Bible gave me
insight from both a nutritional and philosophical standpoint."*

—Dr. Robert Goldman M.D., Ph.D,DO, FAASP
World Chairman-International Medical Commission
Founder & Chairman-International Sports Hall of Fame

TAKE TWO TABLETS *is essential to understand not only what the Bible
teaches on doctrine and belief but also on ancient knowledge to help us live better for a longer time. It also contains a philosophical angle that challenges your
original convictions; you're not the same after reading it.*

—Dr. Edmundo Muniz M.D./Ph.D.
CEO Certara Inc.

God, our Creator and Great Physician, clearly prescribed health solutions for us in the Bible in ways we can easily verify them using modern scientific methods. For example, because we were created as vegetarians, we might predict that a vegetarian diet would be a perfect diet: several medical studies now confirm this. Fasting and laughter for better health are also Biblical predictions. If you want to benefit from God's medical truths, you will benefit extraordinarily from reading TAKE TWO TABLETS.

—Aaron Tabor, MD
Graduate of The Johns Hopkins School
of Medicine; Founder of <u>JesusDaily.com</u>

TAKE TWO TABLETS

TAKE TWO TABLETS

MEDICINE FROM THE BIBLE

PETER M. KASH, ED.D.

SHMUEL EINAV, PH.D.

LINDA FRIEDLAND, M.D.

White River Press
Amherst, Massachusetts

Take Two Tablets: Medicine from the Bible
Copyright 2016 Peter Kash and Kinneret Zmora Publishing House
All rights reserved.

First published in Hebrew in 2014 by Kinneret Zmora Publishing House

First published in English in 2016 by
White River Press
P.O. Box 3561
Amherst, Massachusetts 01004
whiteriverpress.com

Front cover image credits:
Moses Received the Tablets of Law. Engraving/photo: copyright Tarker/Bridgemanimages.
Pills: ajt/Shutterstock

ISBN:978-1-887043-22-9

Library of Congress Cataloging-in-Publication Data

Names: Kash, Peter Morgan, author. | Einav, Shmuel, 1942 - , author. | Friedland, Linda,
    1964- , author.
Title: Take two tablets : medicine from the Bible / Peter M. Kash, Shmuel Einav, Linda Friedland.
Other titles: Luot ha-berit. English
Description: First English language edition. | Amherst, Massachusetts : White River Press, [2016]
Identifiers: LCCN 2015047753 | ISBN 9781887043229 (pbk. : alk. paper)
Subjects: | MESH: Bible. | Medicine in Literature | Religion and Medicine
Classification: LCC BL65.M4 | NLM WZ 330 | DDC 201/.661--dc23
LC record available at http://lccn.loc.gov/2015047753

Acknowledgements

I am indebted to my wife Hassia for her continuous support and collaboration while writing this book. My daughters Gali, Noya, and Rona and my granddaughters Roni-Tzoof, Aya, Libi, and Alma were an integral part of my efforts. Last but not least, I thank my co-author Peter, with whom I spent hundreds of hours as we banged our heads together, and from whom I learned the art of writing for the public and for providing me with the opportunity to prove my knowledge of the Bible.

— *Dr. Shmuel Einav*

This being my third book, it goes without saying that without the support of my wife, Donna, and our children Jared, Colby, Shantal, and Zena, the five years spent in the research and writing of this book would not have been as productive and joyous. Working with Shmuel, I learned so much from his sage advice and life experience that he became a true, enduring friend. I would also like to thank Ziv Lewis and Kinneret Zmora for believing in this book and for sharing it internationally. I also want to thank Linda Roghaar of White River Press and Jean Stone for very professional editing and a great experience in sharing this book with the masses. Lastly, thanks go out to our friend and colleague Dr. Linda Friedland, who brought greater knowledge and editing skills that frankly made the book that much better.

— *Dr. Peter Kash*

Peter and Shmuel have created a magnificent manuscript. Gratitude to our Creator for connecting me with Dr. Peter Kash. It was an honor and privilege for me to collaborate, edit, rework, and add some insights on this subject about which I am passionate. After the writing of five previous medical, health, and lifestyle books, it was a joy to work through this glorious integration of science, life, and the Bible. I hope my husband, Peter, children Gavriel (and Lee), Leora, Yael (and David), Aharon, and Benjamin, and grandsons Zachary and Samuel will be inspired by this work.

—*Dr. Linda Friedland*

Contents

Introduction xv

Foreword: Dr. Linda Friedland xix

Biblical Perspective: Dr. Shoshi xxi

Chapter 1: Longevity 1
An Overview of the Historical Record 1
Until 120 2
70-Year Lifespan 3
Contributing Factors to Biblical Longevity 4
Links to Longevity 4
Secrets of Longevity and the Laron Syndrome 6
Fasting in Ancient Pathways and New Science 6
Technology and Longevity into the Future 7
Reality of Chronic Diseases of Lifestyle 8
Sometimes the Answer Is "No" 8
Finding Clues in Other Species 9
Immortality, Karma, and Reincarnation 10
Telomeres and DNA 11

Chapter 2: Nutrition in the Bible 12
A Biblical Guide to Good Health 12
Superfoods and the Bible 12
A Sensible Food Plan: Meat Eating or Vegetarian? 13

Meat-Free: Healthy or Deficient? 14
The Bible: An Ancient Source for the Modern Diet.................14
Olive Oil 15
The Mediterranean Diet...16
A Few Words about Figs...17
Nature's Vibrant Colors: Antioxidants in the Bible? 18
The Honey Factor...18
Dates and Pomegranates: Ancient Fruits,
      Modern Wonders..19
Wine and Grapes: Sacred Substance 20
Kale and the Eco-Green Bible..20
Holy Food 21
      Citron...21
      Lentils..21
      Nuts..21
      Apples...22
      Chickpeas...23
      Ancient Seeds 23
      Blackberries...24
      Cinnamon...24
      Garlic..24
      Onions and Leeks 25
More on Phytochemicals: Bursts of Energetic Color 25
      Carotenoids..25
      Lycopene 26
      Lutein 26
      Anthocyanins...26
      Flavonoids 26
Minerals and Healing Substances 26
Breast Milk 27
The Power of Water 28
Science, the Bible, and Maimonides 28

Chapter 3: Sex in the Bible 30
The Purpose of It All..30

Biblical Sex and the Song of Songs 30
The Health Effects of Sex...31
The Benefits of Frequent Sex...32
Sex, the Brain, and Memory..32
Kissing in the Bible...32
The Science of Kissing 33
Breasts...34
What about Her Hair?..34
The Knowing Nose 35
Fertility..35
Biblical Commentaries on the Importance of Sex 36
Respect and Women's Rights..37
Monogamy 38
Evolving into God's Image..38

Chapter 4: Ancient Healing Pathways 40
Universal Common Truths...40
Hebrew Medicine...40
Love thy Neighbor: A Dream of Harmony and Peace 41
Respect for all Human Life 42
We are all from the same DNA 43
Enlightenment..43
Buddhism and Judaism: A Brief Comparison......................43
Buddhism, Chinese, and Western Medicine.........................45
The Buddha as the Great Doctor and Maimonides 46
Repentance and Confession 46
Christian Healing...47
Indigenous Aboriginal Culture and Healing.........................48
Three Body Types, Four Elements, Six Realms,
    Ten Emanations 49
Imbalance of the Four Elements 50
Chinese Medicine: Acupuncture,
    Medicinals, and Energy 51
Pulse Points: Jewish Kabbalah, Ayurveda,
    and Traditional Chinese Medicine 52

Judaism and Confucianism: Where did they Intersect? 53
Disease is not Divine Punishment 54
Restoration and Healing from Disease............................55

Chapter 5: Joy and Laughter;
  Pain and Suffering...56
Laughter and Pain 56
The Best Medicine 56
A Treatment for Pain?..57
Jewish Humor: A Vaccine against Suffering....................58
Health Outcomes of Humor and Laughter....................59
The Science of Humor 60
Joy and Laughter throughout History............................60
A Neurological Approach to Laughter and Joy.............61
Communication is What it's All About............................62
Inappropriate Humor and Embarrassment.....................63
Pain and Pain Syndromes..63
Pain Killers in the Bible..64

Chapter 6: Preventive Medicine in the Bible 66
A Worldwide Crisis 66
Take Personal Responsibility...66
The Bible and Talmud: Repository of
  Medical Wisdom...67
Preventive Medicine in the Bible 68
Jewish Dietary Laws: A Jewish Approach
  to Healthcare...68
Food Hygiene 70
Health Rules of the Bible and Talmud............................70
The Bible and Public Health 72
The Origin of the Word *Quarantine*................................73
Hygiene and Infection Control..73
Hand Washing: Way Before Medical Science 74
Healing from Minerals and Sea Salt 75
Ritual Baths..76

Circumcision 76
Public Health References throughout the Bible............................78
Maimonides and Preventive Health 78

Chapter 7: Work and Stress 79
Work: Meaningful Fulfillment or Curse?....................................79
Stressed-Out: A Universal Malady...79
Not all Stress is Bad..80
Is Stress a Mental State?...80
The Stress Response..80
Chronic Adaptation to Stress..81
The Daily Grind..82
A Divinely Ordained Antidote for Stress....................................82
The Science of Rest...83
A Call to Rest..83
A Badge of Honor..84
An Example from the Bible: Saul and David 84
Building Resilience 85
The Illusion of Control 86
Leadership and Stress: A Lesson from King David 87
Ask for Help and Advice: A Lesson from Moses..........................87
Stress and Work..88
Pay on Time! 88
Work: Boredom or Satisfaction? Ecclesiastes..............................89
Work as a Commandment; Work as a Blessing 90
A Rhythm of Work and Rest 90
The Causes of Chronic Stress..91
Stress: A Threat to Health in Biblical Times and Now................91
Depression and Suicide...92
Stress-Relieving Strategies..93
Self-Awareness and Loving-Kindness 94
Exercise..94
Optimal Nutrition...95
Music...96
Meditation 96

Chapter 8: Medical Ethics 97
The Sanctity of Life..97
First, Do No Harm..97
Doctor-Patient Relationship...98
Healing...99
The Obligation to Heal..99
Morality..100
Protecting the Environment...101
Environmental Sustainability...101
Ethics and Responsible Practice..102
Medical Dilemmas 103
The Biblical View on Euthanasia 103

Chapter 9: The Future of Medicine—
    Becoming God? 106
Future Science 106
The Hidden Source..106
Stem Cell Research...107
Mini Brains..108
New Blood Vessels 108
Personalization: From Genomics to Proteomics 109
Regenerative Medicine...110
Creation of Organs: From Dream to Reality 110
Creation of Eve from Adam's Rib 111
Goethe's *Faust*: Creating Man 112
Mary Shelly's *Frankenstein* 113
Prosthetics and Reconstruction 113
Tissue Engineering...114
Regenerative Medicine...115
Organ Transplantation 116
Potential Technological Advances in the
    Future of Medicine...117
You're Unique...119
P4 Medicine 119
Bionic Man...120

Mind Boggling..121
The War on Cancer..122
The Tree of Knowledge; The Tree of Healing...........123
Gene Therapy and Cancer..124
The Future Is Around the Corner.................................125
Vaccines and Cancer..125
Alzheimer's Disease and the Bible.................................126

Epilogue...129
What Have We Accomplished?.....................................129

Introduction

The journey that led to the writing of *Take Two Tablets: Medicine from the Bible* began nearly five years before the manuscript was started. Dr. Shmuel Einav and Dr. Peter Kash met for the first time as panel members at a conference in New York; they had gathered with colleagues to discuss the future of science on behalf of Tel Aviv University. They spoke at length that day and discovered that they were each writing a similar text, and so they decided to collaborate on this project.

They were both writing about "The Book," the one that depicts the origin of the universe and all that is in it; "The Good Book" as some would refer to it. To their surprise, in this hectic, fast-paced world, their book took them almost five years to research, write, edit, translate, proofread, publish, distribute, and place joyfully into your hands.

Their purpose in this endeavor is to share with readers an aspect of the Bible that, throughout the generations, has not often been exposed: the correlation of medicine, healing, and well-being. Their stated goal is not to impose any subjective opinions; rather, to provide clear and concise interpretations, interfaced with science and overlapping with other ancient wisdoms. Indeed, every now and then, you may find a statement that will not seem completely objective and this may reflect the author's voice or narrative, which will be indicated as such. Their aim, however, is simply to look at the Bible as a guide not only to living but also to adding to quality of life, both physically and spiritually.

Rough estimates state that the Bible and various sections of it have been translated into more than 2,018 languages, and it is believed that over the course of human history, there may have been as many as 30,000 translations into languages or dialects of a common language. Throughout history, billions of people have read what is often referred to as the Old Testament. The reality is that 'Old' is a misnomer as "The Good Book" is neither from the past nor the future; the intent is that it is always to be read and understood in the present, because the ethos and concepts are alive and dynamic. The Bible is a compass that indicates how human beings can survive physically and physiologically, evolving on many levels and developing themselves in the image of God. The authors hope that if you as the reader can learn one or two new ideas from the underlying messages shared here from the integration of the Bible and modern science and can thereby enhance your lives and the lives of those around you, then the many collective years of endeavor will have been worth the effort.

The diverse topics address the wide range of connectedness of all healing pathways of religions, nutrition, sex and longevity, medical ethics, stress, and the future of man. The authors wrote and rewrote numerous drafts in order to find elements that would interest you all: worldly readers, medical doctors and scientists; religious philosophers and secular thinkers; and biblical scholars, atheists, and the faithful from across the spectrum of world religions and cultures.

"When we decided to write this manuscript dealing with many serious topics such as life and death and sex, we wanted the book to carry some lighthearted, energy, so you could simply *enjoy!*" Dr. Kash explained.

Dr. Shosh Shapira, the biblical scholar who has reviewed this work said, "The book by Dr. Kash and Prof. Einav brings together two worlds seemingly foreign to each other—the ancient world of the Bible and the modern scientific world—in a fresh and original approach. The term 'People of the Book' was given to People of

Israel not only because of the original Bible, but also because the 'book' is the axis of their historical and cultural existence. With the destruction of the Second Temple, Jewish life moved from the Holy Temple worship to the biblical school, a place of books and learning, which continues until today."

Dr. Kash often reminds his children: "Knowledge that is not shared is simply knowledge; but when it is shared, it becomes wisdom." *Dr. Einav* is a world-renowned educator, researcher, and inventor. It is his hope that this book will be a legacy, not only to his own grandchildren but also to *all* future generations.

Together, Dr. Kash and Dr. Einav believe that, as humanity unfolds, there can be no greater guide to our history, to teach us where we came from, than The Good Book. Their hope is that it will continue to illuminate our way and help us fulfill our purpose, both as individuals and as citizens of the world.

Dr. Linda Friedland joined Drs. Kash and Einav after writing on similar topics for over 20 years. The author of five bestsellers, Dr. Friedland has reworked, edited, and reviewed this entire manuscript repeatedly and has included some of her own original concepts and commentary throughout.

A percentage of the proceeds from this book will be donated to a cancer charity in each country where it is published.

Foreword

"Heal us . . . and we will be healed. Send complete healing for all our ailments for You are God, the faithful and compassionate Healer."
Jeremiah 17:14

In the crafting of *Take Two Tablets*, Dr. Peter Kash and Professor Shmuel Einav have created a masterpiece. The intertwining of cutting-edge scientific data with profound biblical insights provides a wonderful narrative. It is filled with much practical application that is more relevant now than ever.

At this time in the world, there is a flood of information about almost all healing pathways, except that of the biblical healing tradition of the Old Testament, which is one of the most ancient and richest sources of wisdom. Throughout the world, medicine, healing and longevity are high on the agenda. We face a dramatic increase in illnesses, particularly chronic diseases of lifestyle, stress related illness, cancer, and depression. Concomitant with this there has been an explosion of interest in many types of alternate medicine pathways and ancient healing modalities.

Although much literature exists on medical bioethics and biblical law, very little contemporary works have been written on the Bible's teachings about actual healing and well-being, a subject about which I am passionate. I was therefore delighted to see this work and honored to write the foreword for this magnificent tome. I also had the privilege of reworking its wonderful sections.

Over the last three decades, a huge body of scientific and clinical evidence has emerged demonstrating the importance of emotional and spiritual factors in physical healing. More and more, medical research is now concentrating on the complex relationship between mind, brain, endocrine and immune systems, and the rest of the body. Increasing numbers of patients are supplementing their medical treatment and well-being strategies with fitness, exercise, nutrition, meditation, prayer, faith, love, and joy—psychological as well as spiritual dimensions to enhance their health and lives. "The best of science is being integrated with emotions, mental state, and spirituality," said Dr. Herbert Benson, cardiologist, and president of the Mind-Body Medical Institute at Harvard Medical School. "We are addressing God and belief through the language of the day, which is science."

The Bible provides a wealth and depth of healing insights and medical anecdotes, which the authors have accessed through many years of research, together with their own endeavors in the world of science. Furthermore, few people know that there is a powerful biblical commandment in the book of Numbers 4:15 to be "exceedingly attentive in preserving our own health."

In the very last prophecy given in the Bible, the prophet Malachi revealed that in time to come a new light will shine into the world, not a physical light, but the spiritual light of true justice, healing, and love that will come to correct the strife and disorder in countries, nations, communities, families, and ultimately within our individual souls and bodies.

Take Two Tablets blends the future of medicine with the ancient healing pathway of the Bible. By reading this book, we can be inspired to heed the ancient call to take responsibility for our own health, and at the same time attempt to draw down this healing light. "Heal us and we will be healed, save us and we will be saved, for You are our true Healer."

Dr. Linda Friedland M.D.
Perth, Australia, January 2016

Biblical Perspective

D r. Kash and Prof. Einav bring together two worlds: the ancient world of the Bible and the modern period.

Take two Tablets fulfills a fresh and original perspective of the "People of the Book" by maintaining that reading the Bible is about finding all that is hidden in it, and that the discovery of the hidden is not just for reading, but has significance on the horizon of human life. This book is a fascinating example of the interpretation of the Bible as a moral code.

God's first appeal to Man (the story of Paradise) is on eating. Genesis 2:16–18, says: "And the LORD God commanded man, saying, "You may surely eat of every tree of the garden, but of the tree of the knowledge of good and evil you shall not eat, for in the day that you eat of it you shall surely die."

Eating sets the boundary between permissible and forbidden. It is a test of whether a person will master his will and exercise his freedom as created in the image of God, or yield to his natural impulses and be like other animals that, like him, were created from the dust of earth. The tree is therefore a test case for Man being as a moral entity, and eating is converted from a need to a value.

Besides the basic existential need of eating, Man was created as a sexual being, in the form of male and female. Eating and sex unite Man with other animals and distinguish him from God, his Creator. Similar to the abundance of food stories, sexuality and sexual stories are frequent through the Bible. The sexual command was given in the Bible even before the myth of paradise: "And you shall be fruitful and multiply, increase greatly on the earth and multiply in it." (Genesis 9: 7)

Food and sex are two basic instincts emphasized in the Bible. The Bible describes in detail the ways that being human elevates them from the animal level to the level of moral existence. Man is not told to torture the body by avoidance, but to please the body through self-control. The relationship between mating and eating food is at the base of biblical language.

Take Two Tablets opens and closes not with the tree of knowledge but the tree of life. It begins with analyzing the longevity of the ten pre-flood generations from Adam to Noah, and ends with a futuristic outlook (not so distant), according to which people can live for many years, perhaps as Methuselah. It also closes the book "The History of Man" in the Bible, which begins with the first story: "In the beginning God Created the heavens and the earth" (Genesis: 1:1); through the second story: "These are the generations of heaven and earth when they were created" (Genesis 2:4); to the third story that begins with the verse: "This is the book of the generations of Adam. When God created Man, he made him in the likeness of God. Male and female he created them, and he blessed them and named them Man when they were created" (Genesis 5:1–2).

The last chapter of *Take Two Tablets* is quantitatively looking into the ability of modern science and scientists to break life barriers. It gives rise to the biblical question: Becoming God? Who and where will set the boundaries? Here again the modern scientist is burdened by biblical interpretation of responsibility, as he is aware that the interpretation is a moral dialogue. The medical pills of Two Tablets are decoding the hidden light of the Two Tablets.

—Dr. Shosh Shapira
Head of Biblical Studies
Levinsky College and Bina College, Tel Aviv

Take Two Tablets

Chapter 1

Longevity

"Knowledge that is not shared is simply knowledge, but when it is shared it becomes Wisdom."

—Dr. Peter Kash

An Overview of the Historical Record

In ancient times, people lived to ages that are well beyond our common experience today. In a world where longevity varies from 35 in some developing countries to 85 in many Western countries, reading about someone who lived to be hundreds of years old is more than just intriguing; it leaves us incredulous. This is particularly fascinating at a time when anti-aging has become a medical specialty and much science has emerged on how to prolong longevity.

The Book of Genesis chronicles some of the historical record from Adam to Noah. God created male and female in his likeness. Adam was 135 when his third son, Seth, was born. He then had other sons and daughters, and altogether he lived to 930. Enosh, the son of Seth, was born when Seth was 105 years old. He had other sons and daughters and lived an additional 807 years; that is, until he was 912 years (Genesis 5:7, 8). And it continues: Kenan was born to Enosh when he was 90 years old; Enosh died at the age of 915. Mahalalel was born to Kenan when he was 70; Kenan

1

lived to the age of 910 years. Jared was born to Mahalalel when he was 65; he then lived to 892 years. Enoch was born to Jared when he was 62; Jared lived a total of 962 years. Methuselah was born to Enoch when he was 65; Enoch lived to 365 years. Methuselah lived to 969 years; when he was 180 years, he had Lemach, who lived 777 years. Finally, Noah became the father of Shem, Ham, and Yapheth when he was 500 years old; he died at 950 years of age (Genesis 5:32, 9:29).

Until 120

This period of extended longevity ended with the flood. In Genesis 6:3: And the Lord said, "My spirit shall not abide in man forever, for that he also is flesh; therefore shall his days be a hundred and twenty years." The limit of human longevity according to science today is also approximately 120 years. This is generally determined by the length of telomeres, which are the tips protecting the DNA of a chromosome from deterioration.

We must ask ourselves: How was it possible before the flood for humankind to have lived so long? An immediate, albeit trivial, answer is that all those details of longevity are simply comprised of myths and legends. A plausible and well-accepted explanation by biblical scholars and agnostics alike is that time was measured by different instrumentation at that time. But there are other factors that could explain the reduction in longevity after the flood. In a world that began with just two people, it would have been necessary for subsequent generations to live longer in order to have and maintain large families. In that way, resources were shifted away from caring for old and sick people in order to enhance the life and surroundings of the vigorous. By the time of the flood, the earth was more densely populated, and people were more dispersed. The flood did not only destroy the animals, but also changed the structure of the earth. The flood caused global differences in climate, hydrology, and atmospheric composition, including cosmic radiation, the ozone layer, UV light, and dietary habits. All of that caused chemical and human physiological changes that resulted in a steep decline of the post-flood lifespan. Yet, even God planned a transition period: The elapsed time from Shem (son of Noah) to Abraham (ten generations) was 317 years. Prior to the flood, ten generations spanned 857 years, a much longer period. Could another possible contributing factor be that all the biblical figures prior to the flood were vegetarians?

It is interesting to note that the exponential decay curve for many populations is similar to the decay curve of the patriarchs. What does this signify? In nature, all things decay at a similar exponential rate, which is depicted as a curve. Comparing the nature decay rate and the patriarch age decay rate, the correlation coefficient is .88, indicating a very close similarity. Moreover, it also indicates that the age decay rate of the patriarchs is not a wishful story of the Bible, but an outcome of natural behavior. Noteworthy, the decay rate of the post-flood patriarchs shows an almost perfect exponential leveling off at the age of 70.

70-Year Lifespan

The familiar 70-year lifespan we read about in Psalms 90:10 is close to what we have returned to in the past century. So, how did people live that long in biblical times? The Bible does not say directly; but it does give us some hints, and we can apply what the Bible says to what we see in nature and see if it makes sense.

First of all, after God created Adam, He said it was "very good" (Genesis 1:31). As opposed to all the other creations which were termed simply 'good.' Thus, Adam's body must have been "very good." That is, the original creation in the form of man/woman was possibly created without or with less of the effects contributing to a shortened lifespan. After thousands of years of evolution, our physical bodies may continue to experience the effects of this shortened life span, continuing to "run down." But as we will see later, perhaps from the beginning of biblical times, we are finally beginning to live beyond what was ever imaginable by modern-day forecasters and even scientists for it seems that not only have we learned from the Tree of Knowledge, it seems that we may have cloned it.

Contributing Factors to Biblical Longevity

How could people live that long? What contributed to their exceptional longevity? The Bible gives us several hints that we can apply and see if it makes sense. Genesis 1:6–7 describes separation of water above and below the firmament. This water separation was a kind of canopy for the earth, making it a much healthier place to live. This sky and atmosphere covered the *earth*. A very popular model that seems to fit the facts of nature and the Bible is the Whitcomb/Morris model, named for two authors who proposed in their book, *The Genesis flood*, (Nutley, NJ: Presbyterian and Reformed Publishing Co., 1961) that this water layer "above" was a vapor canopy. Such a canopy could have protected people, animals, and vegetation from the damaging effects of radiation. Most likely, this water "above" somehow served as a protective blanket for the earth, making it a much healthier place to live. Hence, the period before the flood was marked by a very pleasant climate. Genesis 2:5, 6, 9 suggest that the early earth did not experience rain; in fact, seasonal cold and heat are not mentioned until after the flood.

In Genesis 7:11, 12, we read that the "floodgates" were opened for 40 days and 40 nights. A worldwide flood required massive amounts of water, and these waters from above, no doubt, contributed to the deluge. Therefore, after the flood, possibly lifespans were shortened by radiation, causing harmful somatic (bodily) effects like cancer, for example, and genetic effects, like mutations.

Links to Longevity

Right now, although there are many centenarians, the vast majority of people are not living healthily until 120 years. However, as science and technology develop ways to clear cells of debris and damage, we will possibly, be able to extend the maximum lifespan, perhaps indefinitely. In fact, two medical researchers, Dr. Pinchas "Hassy" Cohen, Dean of the University of Southern California, Leonard School of Gerontology, and Dr. Nir Barzilai, Director of the Institute for Aging Research at the Albert Einstein College of Medicine in New York, have worked on the Longevity Gene

Project since 1998. In a study that followed some 2,000 patients, all over age 90, who had siblings also over age 90, researchers discovered specific genes that lead to aging, specifically a variant gene that leads to a higher HDL (good cholesterol). Their data is overwhelming and yielded correlations between specific genes and longevity, as measured by decreases in diabetes and heart disease. Just as important is that their offspring have more than a 300 percent greater chance of becoming centenarians than those without parents carrying these genes. They are isolating the genes responsible for longevity and ultimately attempting to create a scientific version of the "fountain of youth."

Other significant research is found in The New England (Harvard) Centenarian Study conducted by Thomas Perls and Margery Sutter. An ongoing study since it was initiated in 1994 on over 5000 participants, the results to date indicate that of the over 50,000 centenarians within the United States, 82% are female. It stipulates that the highest ratio of centenarians in the world is in Okinawa, of which 90% are female; and that, according to United Nation data, by 2050 there will be 2.2 million centenarians in the world: 472,000 of whom will be from China; 298,000 from the U.S.; 272,000 from Japan; and 111,000 from India. With about 300,000 people in the world today living over 100 years of age, the number is growing exponentially. This study has demonstrated that although genes do play a role, there are powerful lifestyle factors in common amongst centenarians. They generally don't smoke and are not obese, lead active lives, may drink alcohol sparingly, and almost all have a positive outlook and feel a deep sense of meaning and purpose in life.

You may recall the 1985 movie *Cocoon*, directed by Ron Howard, in which a pool with specialized water, used by aliens from another time, seems to energize present-day senior citizens who swim in the pool. Will such future medical technology allow us to reach the age of Methuselah?

Secrets of Longevity and the Laron Syndrome

What is the secret of longevity? People living in remote villages in Ecuador were found to have a mutation that may shed some light on human longevity and ways to increase it. These villagers are very short in stature, only about a meter tall, and they manifest a rare condition known as the Laron syndrome or Laron-type dwarfism. It is named after Zvi Laron, the Israeli researcher who, with A. Pertzelan and S. Mannheimer, first reported the condition in 1966. It is characterized by insensitivity to growth hormone (GH). Since then, severe resistance to GH, characterized by grossly impaired growth despite normal levels of GH in serum, has been termed Laron syndrome. These villagers are probably the descendants of Sephardic Jews from Spain and Portugal. They are almost completely free of two age-related diseases, cancer and diabetes. The Laron patients' cells make very little Insulin-like Growth Factor—IGF-1—so, as a result, very little IGF-1 signaling takes place. Therefore, the Laron patients are expected to live much longer. This mutation seems to have enabled them, perhaps through a fortunate combination of lifestyle, genetics, and pure statistical chance, to survive to an extreme point up to and beyond the 120-year barrier.

Fasting in Ancient Pathways and New Science

There is a huge body of scientific data demonstrating the effects of fasting on extending life. Although there are many lifestyle factors that may contribute to longevity, the significant caloric restriction through fasting is one of the only proven methods of extending life. Fasting is a traditional spiritual practice among the people of The Book. There are numerous biblical references to fasting. In Exodus 34:28, we read of Moses: "...he was there with the Lord forty days and forty nights; he did not eat bread or drink water." Leviticus 23:26: "Now on the tenth day of this seventh month is the Day of Atonement. It shall be for you a time of holy convocation, and you shall afflict yourselves and present a food offering to the Lord. And you shall not do any work on that very day, for it is a Day of Atonement, to make atonement for you before the Lord your God." This does not mean you need to begin fasting in order to live longer. Much research still needs to take place in the field of what is called "Caloric Restriction." It does mean cutting back on gluttony and overeating, which is being tackled by all responsible medical establishments as we face a massive obesity epidemic.

There are six fast days in the Jewish calendar including the Day of Atonement, the Fast of Esther, Tishah b'Av (a day of mourning for the destruction of both Temples in Jerusalem), the Fast of Gedaliah, which recalls the assassination of the governor of Judah during the period of the First Temple ending Jewish autonomy after the destruction of Temple by Babylonia some 2,500 years ago, and two others commemorating calamitous events. Fasting is a common practice among most cultures and faith groups as well. The Greeks practiced fasting. Plato and Socrates are reported to have fasted, and Pythagoras required his students to fast before studying. Muslims fast from dawn to dusk for a 30-day period during Ramadan. Christians may fast at times during Lent, a 40-day period, or make a commitment to avoid certain foods, perhaps to spiritually connect to the 40 days that Jesus fasted. Various sects of Hindus fast; the Maha Shivaratree observe fasting for nine days, twice a year. Buddhists practice fasting for self-discipline and purification; consuming food during the morning only and during retreats, they fast for days or even weeks with only water. The scientific community is unraveling the mystery of longevity and it seems that fasting certainly plays a role.

Technology and Longevity into the Future

There are many predictions by futurists in this area. Three pioneers in modern science provide a glimpse of the possible future. Ray Kurzweil, the well-known futurist, says that those who succeed to live a little bit longer will be able to benefit from extreme life extension. Dr. Aubrey de Grey, author in the field of gerontology, editor-in-chief of the academic journal *Rejuvenation Research*, believes that a person born today may live beyond 150 years of age. However, the experts underlined that, while gradually, the human lifespan is heading toward some radical gains, it will not be as soon as has been predicted. The strong commitment of the scientific community in the field of nanotechnology, particularly in terms of stem cell research, tissue engineering and regenerative medicine, will help scientists break new ground in engineering of health treatments and medications. For instance, Ian Pearson of the British Institute of Nanotechnology and the founder of Futurizon believes (contrary to most other scientists) in an almost infinite lifespan.

People may be given the option to live longer lives in the future or choose not to do so, as medication to increase longevity may come to exist. Scientific research, such as genetic engineering, nanotechnology, and other technological advances tend to promote healthy living and longevity. Food may also contribute to a significant change in human health.

Reality of Chronic Diseases of Lifestyle

Although medical science has contributed to increased life expectancy, we still require a strong medical model to contend with significant illness due to chronic diseases of lifestyle and infirmity in later years related to cardiovascular disease and many other age-related illnesses. Extending life for the sake of longevity has little value unless accompanied by robust health and a good quality of life. Therefore the quest for extending longevity should go hand in hand with promoting physical, mental, and spiritual well-being throughout.

Sometimes the Answer Is "No"

The Bible provides us with examples about how to enhance the quality of our daily lives, no matter what our particular religion or belief system is. Here is Moses, a prophet who is revered by all major religions, the only one, in fact, to actually see God, face to face. Moses' only request of God was to visit the Land of Israel, the land of his forefathers, Abraham, Isaac, and Jacob. Most scholars believe that Moses didn't enter the Land of Israel because at Meribah (Numbers 20:7–12), when Israel complained and cried out for water, Moses lectured the nation harshly and unnecessarily, and later, Moses disobeyed God by angrily striking the rock twice, instead of just speaking to the rock as God had told him to do. Is there a deeper lesson here?

All of us ask for things from God from success in business to more serious prayers for health of loved ones. We can have greater peace of mind when we realize that even Moses was denied his request; so sometimes when we ask but don't hear a reply we accept that sometimes the answer is "no" for reasons we are incapable of understanding.

Finding Clues in Other Species

The Bible discusses numerous living organisms in addition to mankind: We have burning bushes, whales, and countless species found in Noah's ark, so let's take a look.

The oldest known living organism is *Turritopsis nutricala,* also known as the "immortal" jellyfish, which can live, theoretically, forever, but lives several hundred years. There are sponges in Antarctica that live up to 10,000 years. Sea grass known as *Posidonia oceanica* can live to be as old as 12,000 to 200,000 years. "Methuselah," a Great Basin bristle-cone pine tree is 4,800 years old; even older are spruce trees found in Dalarna, Sweden, at almost 9,550 years of age. Then we have Adwaita, a Aldabra giant tortoise that lived to be 255 years; Tuimalilia, a radiated tortoise, 188 years old; and Harriet, a Galapagos turtle that lived to be 111 years of age. Other species, like a beautiful, blue-and-yellow Macaw in South America, can live to 110 years; Lin Wang, the oldest known elephant, lived to 86 years of age, when most elephants live to 50 years; bowhead whales can live over 210 years; and the Greenland shark also lives more than 200 years.

Immortality, Karma, and Reincarnation

Although physical mortality is a near certainty, most religions have something to say about immortality. In some it means the everlasting nature of the soul, in others it refers to life hereafter, and yet others consider it reincarnation.

There are many possible responses because different belief systems have various expressions on the purpose of life. Most religions do agree that each soul is separated from its physical body at the end of life.

For those who believe in reincarnation, immortality would hinder the evolution of moving through different stages by detaching the physical body and the soul. This applies both to Hinduism and Buddhism, where the soul has to travel through various stages to learn lessons and achieve fulfillment. Jewish theology too, believes in the reincarnation of souls through many lifetimes. This movement of the soul is influenced by karma, which is determined by our actions and reactions in this world. In other words, karma determines our next phase, and if we were to become immortal, then karma would lose its strength to support good deeds.

Human immortality would necessitate that we be eternally conformed to our body as if we are captive in it. We would have limited possibilities to engage in spiritual learning, be prohibited from reaching Nirvana, and thus be prevented from learning our final purpose of existence and reaching our final stage. Some say that physical immortality provides the possibility to steadily learn in one very long lifespan, but limits the pleasure of it to a single body, religion, and society.

Another consideration is that if we are all immortal, should human birth continue? Because the earth's resources limit us, unless we could travel to another solar system, new births should cease to exist. Most religious belief and faith suggest that righteousness and loving-kindness brings us to some form of paradise where we can be with God; yet immortality would render this obsolete. In the Abrahamic faiths, the final stage of life is either in (some form) of hell or heaven. The destination is rationally determined by our ethical behavior.

The first commandment in the Bible given to human beings is the command to procreate. We were commanded to increase our population, and since we were expelled from the Garden of Eden, we have reached seven billion and are still increasing our numbers. However, when Moses came with the new list given by God, multiplying wasn't even mentioned in the top ten of the commandments. Why? Are we to assume that, ultimately, if mankind evolves, not just intellectually but ethically, and we are created in God's image, that we will be able to create some form of immortality, thus negating the need for further births?

Telomeres and DNA

Are there any verses that talk about immortality on earth in the Bible? There is always an assumption of limited life, expressed in the form of lifespan. But there is no prescribed limit: A period of 70 years is noted in the time before the flood in Genesis. Other long-lived prophets were Abraham, who reached 140 years; Moses, 120 years; and David, 70 years. However, nothing in the Bible mentions that humans shouldn't or couldn't live longer. Each of us has telomeres that can go through 2,000 sequences of divisions. As scientists learn to control the mitosis of cancer cells, these nano "biological clocks" may one day be controlled. Each one of us ponders why we are here and what our purpose is: The Bible gives us hidden insights to be explored and challenged.

All mankind would desire to conquer disease and famine. And almost all peace-loving humans would yearn to witness the prophecy from Isaiah 2:4: "He will judge between the nations and will settle disputes for many peoples. They will beat their swords into plowshares and their spears into pruning hooks. Nation will not take up sword against nation, nor will we have war anymore."

Chapter 2

Nutrition in the Bible

A Biblical Guide to Good Health

"For the Lord your God is bringing you into a good land, a land of brooks of water, of fountains and springs, flowing out in the valleys and hills, a land of wheat and barley, of vines and fig trees and pomegranates, a land of olive trees and honey, a land in which you will eat bread without scarcity, in which you will lack nothing . . . , and you shall eat and be full, and you shall bless the Lord your God for the good land he has given you" (Deuteronomy 8:7).

In a discussion on nutrition from the Bible, which was handed down almost 4,000 years ago, there is no better place to start than at the beginning. In Genesis 1:29, God commands man to only eat fruits and vegetables. He goes on to tell us, "Behold, I have given you every plant yielding seed that is on the surface of all the earth, and every tree which has fruit yielding seed; it shall be food for you."

Superfoods and the Bible

Many foodstuffs are mentioned throughout the Bible starting with heavenly Manna right through to seeds, berries, and a vast array of spices and herbs. Most remarkable is the fact that many of today's most popular and well-researched Superfoods (*also called Power foods or Healing foods*) that doctors and nutritional experts encourage us to eat were cited in the Bible 4,000 years ago. Pomegranates, blackberries, blueberries, honey, barley, lentils, millet, spelt, figs, grapes, and olive oil run throughout the biblical narrative and are now believed to be among the finest foods that we can eat!

A Sensible Food Plan: Meat Eating or Vegetarian?

There is no doubt that from the very beginning of Genesis that Adam and all humanity were vegetarians. Biblical narrative explains how meat eating was only permitted or evolved after Noah and the flood. Many will argue that vegetarianism is the ultimate and that we will come back to that state. Others argue that meat eating came higher up in the order of things and is here to stay. Notwithstanding one's standpoint, the highest nutritional value of plant-based foods is indisputable. Moreover it is the only aspect of nutrition upon which all the experts agree.

There is little doubt that humans were originally programmed for vegetarian lifestyles. With time and unfolding of thousands of years, the Bible allows meat consumption, but not an *eat all you want* approach. The laws are shared with a deep sensitivity towards living beings and the attempt to avoid cruelty. Eating meat is also spoken of within the Bible as allowed for festive occasions and Sabbath as well as with discretion. There is an enormous amount of guidance within the Bible dietary laws.

Contemporary science has demonstrated that vegetarians are thought to suffer from fewer heart attacks, cardiovascular disease, and colon cancers. Vegetarians and pescatarians (those who eat fish but no meat) may suffer less frequently from various illnesses such as appendicitis, kidney disease, and certain cancers. Leviticus 7:23 reads, "Speak unto the children of Israel, saying, 'Ye shall eat no manner of fat, of ox, or of sheep, or of goat"; and verse 7:24 states, "And the fat of the beast that dieth of itself, and the fat of that which is torn with beasts, may be used in any other use: but ye shall in no way eat of it." Later, in Leviticus 7:26: "Never eat the blood of any bird or animal no matter where you live." So, even if you were to eat meat (the Bible verses indicate recognition of mankind's desire for it), there were still prohibitions connected with this practice. The Jewish dietary laws (kosher laws) outline very specifically what types of animals are permitted, how they are to be (humanely) killed and how to prepare and sanctify the eating of meat. It is in no ways meant to be a gluttonous indulgent experience.

Meat-Free: Healthy or Deficient?

Although the intention of the dietary laws was purely for spiritual benefits, many of these restrictions provide profound health benefits.

There is certainly data demonstrating that excessive meat intake and harmful fats are toxic and may lead to adverse health outcomes. However, small to moderate amounts of meat in the diet is valuable as it replenishes iron, folate, and vitamin B12 stores. In a purely vegetarian or vegan diet it is difficult to obtain enough B12 and therefore supplementation is advised. Some good sources for vegetarians are eggs and cheese, but even they may not be enough. Cobalamin (vitamin B12) is important for enhancing memory and preventing fatigue and depression. In biblical times, vegetarians probably received adequate vitamin B nutrients because virtually everything they ate was truly organic; plants and vegetables were being naturally fertilized with stools from animals that contain the bacteria responsible for the production of vitamin B12. Except for the very beginning of biblical times, during most of the period of the Bible, people were non-vegetarians and vitamin B-12 came from liver and red meat, which God saw humans desiring, as is written in Deuteronomy 12:20: "When the Lord your God enlarges your territory, as He has promised you, and you say, 'I will eat meat,' because you crave meat, you may eat meat whenever you desire."

The Bible: An Ancient Source for the Modern Diet

What kinds of foods and fruits were found in biblical times? In Deuteronomy 8:8, we learn of "a land of wheat, barley, of vines and fig trees, and pomegranates, a land of olive oil and honey." It doesn't get better than that when it comes to superfoods and your health.

The Book of Ezekiel specifically recommends eating wheat, barley, beans, lentils, millet, and spelt. By sheer observation, the elders knew which foods had high concentration of protein. In fact, in Ezekiel 4:9, it says: "Take also unto thee wheat and barley and beans and lentils and millet and spelt, and put them in one vessel . . ." Thus, there are 18 amino acids in Ezekiel's "recipe" for bread, along with specific vitamins from the B family, including vitamin B2, B5, and B6, all with specific functions, known now to possibly inhibit depression and boost nervous system efficiency.

And how many times have doctors encouraged patients to increase their fiber intake? Well, 3,500 years ago it was already being recommended. Understanding the implications of consuming a diet of grains, even in these times of low carb diets, may help minimize the risk of colon cancer, ward off osteoporosis, and prevent gallstones. The consumption of folic acid found in high concentrations in these foodstuffs helps prevent birth defects; and eating barley is suggested for insulin maintenance and diabetes control. The remarkable thing is that dieticians and nutritionists everywhere are recommending "ancient grains" such as those mentioned first in the Old Testament; spelt, millet, and the like for their superb nutritional values.

Olive Oil

Olive oil is a wonderful fat. Monounsaturated fats—of which olive oil, avocados, and macadamia nuts are composed—are the best choice of fat. Olive (in Hebrew, *zayit*) is mentioned frequently throughout the Bible: in Genesis, Exodus, Leviticus, and Deuteronomy. In addition to its ritual uses, olive oil was used as a cosmetic, a great source of food and, of course, for medicinal purposes. In biblical times, olive oil was used to treat wounds, ulcer, boils, and pain, and even for inflammation of the gums. Olives contain polyphenols, which may help fight infection. Olive oil may also lower overall cholesterol and help in blood clotting and controlling blood sugar. It is a known phytoestrogen that may help minimize bone density loss, a common occurrence in older women.

The Mediterranean Diet

Long before the term "Mediterranean Diet" came into vogue in the 1990s, the ancient Hebrews, along with the Greeks, were eating the so-called Mediterranean diet. According to Wikipedia, recent evidence demonstrates the overall positive aspects of such a diet: A recent randomized Spanish trial of diet patterns, published in the *New England Journal of Medicine* in 2013, followed almost 7,500 individuals over a period of approximately five years. The study found that individuals on a Mediterranean diet, supplemented with mixed nuts and olive oil, had a 30 percent reduction in risk of a major cardiovascular event and a 49 percent decrease in stroke risk. Subjects followed one of three different diets: a low fat diet; a Mediterranean diet with 50 ml of extra virgin olive oil daily; or a Mediterranean diet with 30 grams of mixed nuts. The nuts were primarily walnuts, which have a high amount of omega-3 fatty acids.

A meta-analysis published in the *British Medical Journal* in 2008 showed that strictly following the Mediterranean diet reduced the risk of dying from cancer and cardiovascular disease as well as the risk of developing Parkinson's and Alzheimer's disease. The results: 9 percent, and 6 percent reductions in overall, cardiovascular, and cancer mortality, respectively. In addition, it was determined that a 13 percent reduction in incidence of Parkinson's and Alzheimer's disease can be expected, provided strict adherence to the diet is observed.

A study published in the *British Medical Journal* in 2009 showed some components of the Mediterranean diet are associated with low risk of mortality. As part of a study on "European Prospective Investigation into Cancer and Nutrition," researchers followed more than 23,000 Greek men and women for 8.5 years to see how various aspects of a Mediterranean diet affect mortality. Moderate alcohol consumption, high fruit and nut consumption, and high legume consumption were also associated with lower risk of mortality. A larger 2011 meta-analysis, published in the *Journal of the American College of Cardiology*, analyzed the results of 50 studies involving more than 500,000 people. It showed a correlation between a Mediterranean diet and lower blood pressure, blood sugar, and triglycerides.

The overwhelming evidence of the use of olives in cleansing rituals dates back to Moses. Olive oil is highlighted for more than just nutritional uses. Olive oil is almost a sacred substance. In Leviticus 8:12, Moses "poured of the anointing oil upon the head of Aaron, and anointed him with oil." Prior to Moses, Jacob (divinely renamed "Israel") made a sacred vow to God after anointing a stone pillar by pouring oil on top of it (Genesis. 28:16-22; 31:13; 35:14). Jacob names the pillar's locale Bet-El, meaning "House of God." Later, almost 1,000 years later, Samuel anoints David as king with a horn of olive oil.

A Few Words about Figs

Figs, mentioned in the Bible, are rich in vitamins A, B1, B2, and potassium and are high in fiber. In Samuel I 30:12, we find: "And they gave him a piece of a cake of figs and two clusters of raisins. And when he had eaten, his spirit revived, for he had not eaten bread or drunk water for three days and three nights." Calcium, which is also found in figs, is helpful in strengthening bones particularly for women. Figs also contain certain amino acids that seem to enhance libido (an interesting effect in light of Adam and Eve's "choice" of fig leaves as garments in Genesis).

Figs have many more properties, including possible protective effects against age-related conditions such as macular degeneration (ARMD), which is the number one cause of loss of vision in adults and Alzheimer's disease. Some preliminary evidence shows that daily intake of figs (together with a diet high in antioxidants as those found in green leafy vegetables) may reduce the onset of ARMD, perhaps up to 30 percent. The leaves of the fig are exhibiting possible anti-diabetic properties by lowering insulin and a possible antihypertensive effect.

Nature's Vibrant Colors: Antioxidants in the Bible?

Did you ever wonder why fruits and vegetables have such bright colors and special aromas that stimulate our olfactory nerve? Perhaps nature wanted to point out for humans and other animal species, "Come over here and consume me."

These colorful fruits and vegetables are among the most important superfoods in our diet. Nature plays a huge role in our diet. We are first attracted to the pigments of these delicious, nutritional, and abundant foods that contain many of the 900 phytochemicals found in nature. Those with the highest concentrations, generally have the brightest colors. In addition, their various scents attract us as well. The Bible mentions many of the superfoods that abound today in our local farmers' markets and fruit stores. It mentions "green" prominently in Genesis 1:30: ". . . to every beast of the earth, to every bird of the air, and to everything that creeps on the earth, in which there is life, I have given every green herb for food." These rich pigments and scents were meant to attract them. Also in Genesis 3:17–18, we find reinforcement for eating plants (vegetables and fruits): ". . . through toil you will eat of it all the days of your life. It will produce thistles for you, and you will eat plants of the field."

The Honey Factor

In the Bible, honey was available from two sources: honeycomb (from beehives) and from dates. Many people are familiar with: ". . . bring them up out of that land into a good and spacious land, a land flowing with milk and honey—the home of the Canaanites, Hittites, Amorites, Perizzites, Hivites, and Jebusites" (Exodus 3:6-8). But honey is mentioned even earlier, in Genesis 43:11 when Israel said: "If it must be, then do this: Put some of the best products of the land in your bags and take them down to the man as a gift—a little balm and a little honey, some spices

and myrrh, some pistachio nuts and almonds." Another source for
honey comes in I Samuel 14:24-27 when Jonathan, son of Saul
was said to have: "reached out the end of the staff that was in his
hand and dipped it into the honeycomb. He raised his hand to his
mouth, and his eyes brightened."

But why honey? Proverbs 24:13 reads: "My son, eat honey, for
it is good, and the drippings of the honeycomb are sweet to your
taste." In addition to its sweet taste, honey has many uses: as a
balm for ailments such as sore throats; as a treatment for insect
bites; and it may even show some possible anti-cancer properties.
Further research shows that honey features:

- flavonoids that display some antioxidant properties;
- antibacterial and anti-fungal properties for which it has
  been used for thousands of years for treating open wounds;
- benefits when used in many detoxification methods and
  energy drinks in Japan;
- relief for some arthritis sufferers when mixed with cider
  vinegar, as encouraged by naturopathic physicians.

In addition to containing vitamin C, calcium, and iron, honey
can be helpful in treating halitosis or bad breath. See Exodus 16:31:
"Now the house of Israel called its name manna. It was like co-
riander seed, white, and the taste of it was like wafers made with
honey."

Dates and Pomegranates: Ancient Fruits, Modern Wonders

In II Samuel 6:19: "He gave a loaf of bread, a cake of dates
and a cake of raisins to each person in the whole crowd of Israelites, both men and women. And all the people went to their
homes." Dates have been around for almost 7,000 years; they are
rich in vitamins, calcium, folate, iron, potassium, magnesium, and
they are great for constipation.

Pomegranates, one of the seven specific species of foods mentioned in Deuteronomy 8:8, are perhaps one of the most valuable

fruits. With amazing health benefits—from possibly preventing plaque buildup in arteries to preventing strokes—pomegranates provide a class of flavonoids that strengthens the immune system. These antioxidants are loaded with enzymes, and there is some anecdotal evidence that its properties may also help inhibit the progression of Alzheimer's and alleviate the symptoms of depression. The ancient Greeks and Romans used pomegranates to cure infestations from tapeworms in the intestine. They are most certainly one of the superfoods of the moment and are loved by chefs the world over for their tart flavor and gorgeous color in salads.

Wine and Grapes: Sacred Substance

Wine is central in the sanctification of the Sabbath, festivals, and special occasions such as circumcision, and is mentioned throughout the Bible. For example, Genesis 9:20 states: "Noah began to be a man of the soil, and he planted a vineyard." Resveratrol, which is found in red grapes, red wine and red grape juice is one of the most powerful of the antioxidants and has shown promising effects in possible prevention of heart diseases, and strokes.

Although red wine is a great source of Resveratrol, excessive intake of red wine or any alcohol undoes all the benefits and can cause significant body and brain damage.

Kale and the Eco-Green Bible

Although the exact translation for Kale is not known for certain in the original Hebrew Bible, there is very little debate that during the biblical ages kale was probably grown and eaten.

Sulphoraphane is the powerful antioxidant substance found in broccoli, spinach, and kale that has been shown anecdotally to be possibly effective in the prevention of colon cancer. Kale is touted as the wonderfood of the moment for its powerful healing properties as well as containing as much as 45% protein. The famous Greek philosopher Theophrastus, a student of Aristotle, spoke of kale. It contains more calcium than milk, more iron than beef per calorie, and more fiber; it has anti-inflammatory properties and is rich in omega-3 and omega-6 fatty acids.

Also known as *Brassica oleracea,* kale grows to maturity in 55 to 60 days versus a cow raised for beef that takes an average of 18 to 24 months. Kale can grow in most climates and is relatively easy and low impact to grow at home or on a farm. To raise one pound of beef requires 16 pounds of grain, 11 times as much fossil fuel, and more than 2,400 gallons of water. Although meat is permitted in the Bible, the intention is for it to be eaten moderately. So the Bible was eco-green 4,000 years before our recent sustainability awareness!

Holy Food
Citron—The rind of citrus fruits contains a powerful antioxidant phytochemical called limonene. The citron or *etrog* (in Hebrew) is the primary citrus fruit mentioned in the Bible. It is a central and sacred item in connection with the festival of the Tabernacles. Leviticus 23:40 reads: "On the first day, you will take for yourselves an etrog of a beautiful tree, date palm branches, twig of a braided tree, and you will rejoice before the Lord your God for seven days." How much more clarity is needed to appreciate the appreciation of nature all around us then this holiday of celebration of a green harvest?

Lentils—We learn in Genesis 25:34 that Jacob gave Esau lentil stew to eat. Lentils are mentioned in a few places throughout the Bible. They are loaded with iron, are a great source of fiber, contain the essential nutrients magnesium and folate, stabilize blood sugar, lower LDL cholesterol, and are a great alternative to red meat.

Nuts—Nuts are mentioned in the Bible in several places. In Genesis 43:11, we find: ". . . take in your containers some of the land's best products, and bring the man a gift—some healing resin, a little

honey, aromatic gum, opium, pistachio nuts and almonds." These
are the only two nuts mentioned in the Bible.

Almonds contain some of the Phytochemicals discussed
above in **Nature's Vibrant Colors**. They are full of fiber, rich in
vitamins E, B6, and folate, and in selenium, magnesium, and zinc,
all of which are essential for cognitive brain function and oleic
acids, which may lower LDL cholesterol.

Pistachio nuts have been around for thousands of years, perhaps first appearing in what are now the geographic areas of Iran,
Syria, and Turkey. Eventually, they ended up in biblical Israel. They
contain monounsaturated and polyunsaturated fats, which may reduce cholesterol levels, the risk of Type 2 diabetes, and cardiovascular disease. Pistachios also have high levels of phosphate, which
contributes to bone and red blood cell production. They are high
in fiber and contain arginine, an important amino acid that serves
as a vasodilator thereby increasing better blood flow particularly
during exercise.

Apples—Central to biblical lore is that the fruit eaten by Adam
and Eve in the Garden of Eden was an apple—but this is not
entirely correct. Although the Bible mentions a tree and a fruit in
Genesis, it never specifies what the particular fruit was. Some say it
could have been a pomegranate. However, in Deuteronomy 32:10,
the text reads: "He found him in a desert land . . . and he kept him
as the apple of his eye."

So why apples? Is the adage, "An apple a day keeps the doctor
away" a biblical prophecy? In reality, perhaps the closest source
we could find is from an 1886 Welsh magazine that states, "Eat an
apple on going to bed, and you'll keep the doctor from earning in
his bread."

Although neither science nor the Bible prescribes eating an
apple a day, it's not a bad idea. There are more than 7,000 varieties
of apples, and each apple has about 5 grams of fiber, vitamin C,

potassium, and specific antioxidants known as phenols, which protect against UVB rays, lower bad cholesterol, and fortify collagen and elastin to preserve your skin. There is even a flavonoid called quercetin, which is only found in apples and is thought to help boost memory. Phlorizin is another apple-based flavonoid: It may help prevent bone loss associated with menopause.

Apples also contain a specific vitamin B, known as B17 within its cores and seeds. When the apple is eaten raw or thrown into a blender thus creating a smoothie, the effects of B17 have demonstrated some promising anti-cancer cell properties.

Chickpeas—As with apples, chickpeas have high concentrations of vitamin B17. The main ingredient of hummus, chickpeas have been around for thousands of years and are still eaten in abundance throughout the Middle East and Israel. Israelis have the highest consumption per capita in the world.

In fact, one of the lesser-known wars between Israel and her Arab neighbors took place when three hundred chefs from Lebanon broke the world's record of the largest plate of hummus — more than 23,042 pounds. This broke the previous record held by an Arab village, Abu Gosh, in Israel, which is known for some of the best hummus in the country.

Ancient Seeds—Until recently, conventional wisdom was that seeds were for discarding or possibly only for planting—but certainly not for consumption. We now know that seeds are often extremely nutritious, examples of which include the sunflower, sesame, chia, and pumpkin seeds (pepitas) that grace many of our modern healthy recipes. But we still seem to discard the seeds of most fruits. According to Genesis 1:29, "God said, "I give you every seed-bearing plant on the face of the whole earth and every tree that has fruit with seed in it. They will be yours for food . . ." Perhaps we shouldn't be discarding these seeds.

The vitamin B17 that is found in apple seeds and chickpeas is also in apricot seeds and paw paw pips (from the South American tropical fruit paw paw). Often called laetrile, it is derived from amygdalin, which contains rhodanese, a powerful enzyme that may hold the key to unlocking the mystery of cancer cell destruction. A complex biochemical pathway that leads to the cell destruction, it is possible that Nature's chemotherapy was known 4,000 years ago. It is amazing that the Bible encourages the nutritional value of seeds that we have been discarding for thousands of years!

Blackberries—Containing many antioxidants and tannin, blackberries grow fairly easily and require little rain. We see this mentioned in Isaiah 5:6: "And I will make it waste; its branches will not be touched with the knife, or the earth worked with the spade; but blackberries and thorns will come up in it: and I will give orders to the clouds not to send rain on it." The high tannin content of blackberries may help relieve intestinal inflammation and stomach disorders.

Cinnamon—Cinnamon is mentioned in Exodus 30:23: "Take the best spices, five hundred shekels' weight of liquid myrrh, and of sweet cinnamon half as much . . ." This provides evidence that for thousands of years, certainly well before the invention of refrigeration, cinnamon was a natural food preservative. A better, healthier sweetener than sugar, cinnamon has anti-inflammatory properties and may be effective for certain yeast infections. In addition, studies have shown that smelling cinnamon may actually improve memory.

Garlic—Garlic is also mentioned in Bible in Numbers 11:5: "We remember the fish we used to eat for free in Egypt. And we had all the cucumbers, melons, leeks, onions, and garlic we wanted." Demonstrated to boost one's immune system it has also been shown that garlic helps reduce cholesterol. It is from a class of sulfur-based compounds that contain allicin, along with vitamins C and B6, selenium, magnesium, potassium, and calcium, which may also inhibit certain cancers cells.

Onions and Leeks—Onions and leeks are also enriched with sulfur-based compounds that have antibacterial properties also serve as anti-clotting mechanisms and help to increase bone density and therefore helpful in prevention of osteoporosis.

More on Phytochemicals: Bursts of Energetic Color

Phytochemicals are protective chemicals found in fruits and vegetables (*phyt-* is from the Greek word for plant or vegetation). They augment immunity and may reduce the risk of cancer and other serious illnesses. The cells of your body are continually exposed to oxidation damage through pollution, chemicals, environmental toxins, smoking, and stress. Oxidation damage causes electrically charged oxygen molecules that can damage tissue; antioxidants mop them up. Phytochemicals provide this antioxidant effect and neutralize the damage; they seem to work together with other compounds rather than each working on its own. They may help slow the aging process and, in addition to cancer, they may also reduce the risk of other diseases, including stroke, heart disease, and osteoporosis.

The cornerstone of optimal nutrition is the abundant consumption of plant-based food, particularly brightly-colored fresh fruits and vegetables as discussed above. These nutrients boost natural energy and protect and heal the body. The recommendations are five to nine servings a day, and should be a combination of fresh, raw vegetables in salads; cooked green, yellow, and orange vegetables; and three or four fruit servings, depending on your particular diet. Among nutrition experts, there is no disagreement about fresh fruits and vegetables: All agree that they are excellent nutrients.

Carotenoids—The specific phytochemicals that contribute to elevated pigment concentrations are called *carotenoids*. These include fruits and vegetables with beta-carotene, such as mangos, broccoli, kale, and pumpkin. All of them seem to have immune-boosting properties thought to possibly inhibit the growth of cancer cells and perhaps even slow the aging process.

Lycopene—Lycopene is strictly speaking a carotenoid and is found in abundance in raw tomatoes and even better in cooked forms such as pasta sauce and ketchup. Lycopene is also found in watermelons, red peppers, grapefruits, and melons, and some very preliminary research suggests they may have a role in preventing prostate disease. Again, along with cucumbers, leeks, onions, and garlic, melons are mentioned in Numbers 11:5: "We remember the fish we used to eat for free in Egypt. And we had all the cucumbers, melons, leeks, onions, and garlic we wanted."

Lutein—Found in spinach, cabbages, and Brussels sprouts, lutein helps improve sight and is thought to be particularly effective in the prevention of macular degeneration and blindness.

Anthocyanins—Anthocyanins are found in blueberries another of the superfoods and may help enhance memory. They are also thought to prevent urinary tract infection.

Flavonoids—Flavonoids neutralize highly unstable free radicals that attack our bodies every day. There is some early evidence that flavonoids reduce inflammation particularly in cancer. They are found in onions, cherries, berries, apples, garlic, as well as citrus fruits, prunes, and green tea. The flavonoids seem to inhibit carcinogenesis (formation of cancer) and cell damage.

Minerals and Healing Substances

Throughout the Bible, we are frequently advised to eat plenty of natural plant-based foods. In addition to containing the phytochemicals mentioned above, they are also rich in many micronutrients and minerals such as magnesium and potassium.

Magnesium—Magnesium is involved in almost all body pathways. It helps regulate melatonin, which promotes a higher quality and longer-lasting sleep cycle, and it may reduce stress. It affects our serotonin levels, which helps to balance mood swings. In turn, it produces IGF-1, which helps strengthen muscles and produces ATP as an energy-booster in our cells. It may loosen tight muscles and increasing flexibility, which is especially important in the later years. Magnesium also stimulates the production of calcitonin, which supports healthy bones. It is regularly used to relieve constipation. By also enhancing insulin secretion, magnesium helps prevent the fastest-growing disease on the planet: type 2 diabetes.

Potassium—Found in abundance in bananas potassium aids the electric activity in the heart, maintains a good blood pressure, and helps prevent the formation of kidney stones. In biblical days, as today, a kidney stone was extremely painful. High-potassium foods include apricots, cod, salmon, and sweet potatoes.

Breast Milk

Nutrition in the Bible has breast milk at its source. Breast milk is possibly the highest quality foodstuff, both physically and spiritually. Breastfeeding— most natural way to deliver a whole host of nutrients—is the method that has allowed human beings to endure and prevail, even while surviving the harshest circumstances of life. Genesis 21:7 states: "Who would have said to Abraham that Sarah would nurse children? Yet I gave him a son in his old age, and the child grew and was weaned . . ."

In Genesis 49:25, Jacob said to Joseph, "Because of your father's God, who helps you . . . blessings of the breast and womb . . ." Later, in Exodus 2:7-10: "Shall I go and call a nurse from the Hebrew women that she may nurse the child?" and Pharaoh's daughter says to Miriam, "Take this child away and nurse him (Moses) and I will give you wages." The Bible also talks about the mother's breasts in terms of comfort, protection, and love; in Song of Songs 8:1: "If only you were like a brother who was nursed at my mother's breast . . ."; in Isaiah 66:10-13: "Rejoice with Jerusalem and be glad for her and all you who love her . . . they may nurse and be satisfied from her consoling breasts."

The fact is that breast milk is perhaps the single greatest source of nutrients to assure an infant's survival. For thousands of years before there were infant formulas, all moms had was an ingenious delivery system, providing a complex formula that is yet to be duplicated even with all the science at our fingertips. Nature provided breast milk to contain complex carbohydrates, or sugars known as *oligosaccharides*. Their importance is so scientifically elegant that women are responsible for the survival of the human race, by passing off these complex sugars to their children that block the adhesion of bacterium to cell surfaces in different parts of the body, thereby inhibiting their attachment and preventing serious illness. In other words, instead of killing the bacteria as antibiotics do, nature understood if there were antibiotics being transferred, eventually the bacterium would have generated a resistance as we are witnessing today around the world. Breast milk is so important for the development of humankind that without it we wouldn't have survived the millennium of evolution.

The Power of Water

Mayim, otherwise known as water or H_2O, is the source of all life: Without it, planet earth, all nature creatures, and humans would cease to exist. The Bible is replete with stories, narratives, and deep explanations and commentaries on water as a source of life but also as a metaphor for love and kindness and deep spirituality uniting the spiritual and physical worlds. Interestingly, the atomic weight for water is "18," and in Kabbalah that signifies "life" and "good luck!"

Science, the Bible, and Maimonides

Ironically, only in the last 20–30 years have we scientifically proven what was stated in the Bible 4,000 years ago. There are commentaries dating back many hundreds of years on these biblical references to nutrition and health. The most famous and profound of these are the writings of Rabbi Moses ben Maimom (1135–1204), who was commonly known as Maimonides or the Rambam. A scientist, astronomer, medical doctor, codifier of Jewish law, rabbinical sage, physician to the Sultan, and prolific writer of commentaries on the Bible which are used and studied by hundreds of thousands daily, his famous work Hanhagat Habriut (*The Pathway to Health*) exists amongst his thousands of other works.

Chapter 3

Sex in the Bible

The Purpose of It All

The Bible's very first commandment is about reproduction and procreation. Genesis 1:28 reads: "Be fruitful and multiply in numbers, fill the earth and subdue it, and you will have dominion over the fish in the sea, and over the birds in the air and over every living thing upon the earth." That this is the very first commandment in the Bible highlights its great significance. The experience of sexuality is far more than a vehicle for procreation. It is also a profound and sacred act of intimacy and is indeed good for our health.

Biblical Sex and The Song of Songs

In the Five Books of Moses, the Bible talks about sexuality more than 200 times. The first general statement is in Genesis 4:1: "And Adam knew his wife and she conceived . . ." Later, in Genesis 2:24, we find: "That is why a man leaves his father and mother and is united to his wife, and they became one flesh." There is frequent reference to sex with the use of the word "knew" and "begot." Abraham "knew" his wife Sarah refers to the sexual act.

Why is sex is mentioned throughout the Bible? A healthy sex life is a foundation of family purity and a health family life. The Song of Songs by King Solomon is not only a holy and profound outpouring of spirituality but also an exquisite love poem. Solomon wrote it for his wife, "a Shulamite." No specific name is given for her, but the name in Arabic means "flame" or "bright," and in Hebrew, it means "peaceful." This poem expressed as a profound love between husband and wife is a metaphor for our love for God. Its power and importance as a central text within the Old Testament is undeniable. Throughout the Old Testament, we see that sex is described as a holy and sacred act, central to the love between two soul mates—especially if the love is like that of Adam and Eve, Solomon and his wife, or David and Bathsheba.

The Bible teaches the importance of true love, which is also connected to being good friends. Biblically speaking, Eve was created for Adam because "It is not good for man to be alone" (Genesis 2:18-23). We began our destiny as human beings at that moment in the Garden of Eden, and we are still evolving, as we struggle to understand the whole purpose of love, marriage, and life.

The Health Effects of Sex

What is clearly apparent is that sex is pleasurable and deeply sustaining for a relationship. Less apparent is its potent effect on health and immunity. Researchers have revealed how a regular sex life may help ward off illness by boosting our immune system. Doctors have discovered that the level of (NK) Natural Killer cells and antibodies that fight infection are much higher in couples that make love regularly. Cortisol, a powerful stress hormone, is suppressed during sexual arousal, making sexual activity a great stress reliever, too. A frequent outpouring of the feel-good factors including endorphins lift depression, blunt anxiety, and leave one with a sense of well-being.

Lovemaking is good for fitness, too. A typical bout of lovemaking is equivalent to sprinting 200 meters. It is demanding on the body, raising one's blood pressure, pulse, and breathing rate. Sexual arousal sparks off the release of neurotransmitters (chemical messengers) in the brain, which stimulate the pituitary gland, the command center for lovemaking. The pituitary also sends messages to the adrenal gland, which starts to produce sex hormones, and within seconds this releases adrenalin, which increases heart rate blood pressure and rapid breathing. Orgasms also induce deeper restorative sleep.

The Benefits of Frequent Sex

The benefits of frequent sex are multiple. Dr. Winnifred Cutler and colleagues from Columbia and Stanford Universities demonstrated the effect of frequent sex on balancing hormones. Frequent sex seems to have an effect on regulating the menstrual cycle. It also boosts levels of estrogen in post-menopausal women, thereby alleviating some of the symptoms of menopause as well as improving bone density and cardiovascular conditioning.

Frequent sex also strengthens the pelvic muscles of women, thereby reducing the risk of urinary incontinence. For men, there is some evidence demonstrating lower rates of prostate disease.

Sex, the Brain, and Memory

Another hormone released during sex is estradiol, which has demonstrated some positive effects on memory and cognitive functioning. It seems to enhance the hippocampus, the part of the brain that is involved in forming, storing, and processing memory.

There is also increasing evidence of the effects of sexual activity on the brain, including the experience of intense olfactory activity (sense of smell), which also enhances memory. Another structure in the brain, the thalamus, serves to relay impulses, particularly sensory information, that not only regulates arousal but also helps to regulate sleep.

Kissing in the Bible

The Hebrew word for "kiss" is *neshikah*, which is also related to the word Hashkah, which means "connection." Genesis 2:7 states: "God fashioned man from the dust of the earth and gave him the breath of life to make him a living being." The Hebrew words for "breath" and "soul" find their source in the Bible and are derived from similar words, *nefesh* and *neshamah*. Kissing is the exchange of one's inner being with that of another. There is some data to suggest that kissing helps to strengthen each other's immune system.

In the Song of Songs 1:1-2, King Solomon's beloved wants him to kiss her: "Let him kiss with the kisses of his mouth." Later, in verse 7, Solomon says, "And your kisses are like the best wine that goes down smoothly, gliding over my lips and teeth."

In verse 4:3 Solomon says to his wife: "Your lips are like crimson thread and your mouth is lovely; your cheeks are like halves of a pomegranate behind your veil." She replies in verse 5:12: "His lips are like lilies, distilling liquid myrrh" (a gum-like substance found in the sap of trees that originated in what is now known as Ethiopia and Yemen).

The Science of Kissing

Why all this kissing? The science of kissing is called "philematology". Kissing reduces levels of cortisol, known as the "stress hormone," in the body and even helps balance and maintain sugar and insulin levels.

Kissing also stimulates the release of oxytocin, the hormone responsible for contractions and childbirth as well as for breast-feeding. Oxytocin is also known as the "hormone of love," because it creates the feelings of warmth and closeness in a relationship. When women breast-feed, oxytocin is also released, along with prolactin, which stimulates the mammary gland to produce breast milk; prolactin is also the protein responsible for the feeling of sexual gratification after sex.

The release of oxytocin during lovemaking facilitates connections on a physiological level through biochemistry and triggers the release of other feel-good neurotransmitters; all of these are related to memory and to emotions that help us relive pleasurable memories from the past, even subconsciously. There is enough evidence from researchers like anthropologist Helen Fisher of Rutgers University on the benefits of open mouth kissing: Open mouth kissing may make it possible for the chemical interactions to increase a woman's fertility as measured by her higher estrogen levels. Testosterone also stimulates the release of dopamine and norepinephrine, which create the feeling of pleasure during kissing. The research reveals that men prefer kissing open mouth and this is thought to transfer and increase their higher levels of testosterone to their kissing partner, which may enhance the female's arousal.

The effects of cuddling are similar to kissing with respect to the release of oxytocin. Again, Solomon and his wife are lying in the vineyards of Ein-Gedi (not far from Masada and the Dead Sea) in verse 1:1 of Song of Songs: "Our couch is green, the beams of our house are cedar, and our rafters are pine"; clearly they are lying together amidst the fields.

Breasts

The Song of Songs is even more explicit when the Shulamite states in the beginning of verse 1:13: "He shall lie all night between my breasts"; then, in chapter 7:7: "Thy stature is like a palm tree and the breasts to a cluster of grapes"; and just one verse later: ". . . I will take hold of the boughs there . . . Also thy breasts shall be clusters of the vine." Song of Songs 7:8 is even more passionately poignant: "Let your breasts be as clusters of grapevine, and the scent of your breath like apples . . ." Later, in the last verses of song 8:1-3: ". . . Oh that thou were as my brother, who sucked the breasts of my mother."

In short, there was no embarrassment in describing the beauty of a loved one's breasts. However, there is an evolutionary scientific basis for men to be attracted to the breasts of women: The primary reason is the unconscious Darwinian understanding that ample breasts can nourish one's offspring.

What about Her Hair?

The hair of many of the biblical women is pictured as long and beautiful. Evolutionary biology may have played a role from the dawn of time when men first realized that women with longer hair were possibly more likely to be better nourished, and thereby better able to care for their future offspring. This trait seemed to be a desirable factor in the selection of a suitable mate. Ezekiel 16:7 reads: "I helped you to flourish like a young plant in the field, and you grew tall and became wonderfully endowed. Your breasts were firm, your hair beautifully thick. And you were completely naked." Hair as a source of attractiveness has been prevalent since the dawn of time.

The Knowing Nose

There is much reference within the biblical text to the sense of smell. It is the sense of smell that helps detect pheromones that indicate sexual and reproductive activity. According to a study by Kate Fox of the Social Issues Research Centre in Oxford, England, during ovulation, a woman's sense of smell can be 1,000 and as much as 10,000 times greater than at other times such as menstruation. This helps women to possibly search out the right male partner to reproduce with. Even sperm cells can detect where to target the egg, based on chemical signaling similar to smell.

Fertility

Around the globe, there has been a significant increase in the rates of infertility. Regardless of whether the primary issue is due to ovulatory failure, hormonal imbalances, structural problems, or sperm pathology, specialists manage the problem of infertility as "a couples' problem." The incidence of male related problems has increased significantly in the last 30 years.

Studies such as the one done by Shiva Dindyal of the Imperial College of Medicine in London showed that since 1940, male sperm count has dropped almost 50%. There are many reasons for this, from increased heat to the testes from tighter underwear and jeans, to more frequent access to hot baths, showers, and Jacuzzis, to more environmental concerns and high levels of daily stress.

According to Dr. Harry Fisch, Professor of Urology at Columbia University Medical Center, obesity also leads to lower sperm count. Much has been written and researched with increased successes in conception rates with all types of infertility; a full discussion on infertility, however, is beyond the scope of this manuscript. Boosting fertility from the biblical sources would highlight the value of high quality nutrition containing essential trace elements necessary for the production of good quality sperm and eggs.

Today we know that eating foods that are abundant with zinc and folic acid may increase fertility. These include eggs, nuts, almonds, and sesame seeds, which contain the amino acid l-arginine, an important building block in sperm production. A decrease in chromium intake has been linked to lower sperm production, so whole grains, which contain chromium, are recommended. Vitamin E and Selenium are also important. Vitamin E is found in nuts, tomatoes, and spinach. Foods with high levels of selenium include Brazil nuts, onions, mushrooms, fish, eggs, sunflower seeds, and poultry. Decreasing alcohol consumption is also good idea when trying to conceive.

Around the time of the ancient Hebrews, the ancient Chinese populated another part of the world. Acupuncture, originally a Chinese practice, dates back to about the same time that the Bible was given to the Jewish people. Acupuncture has been used successfully in numerous fertility studies with startling results: The data from these studies show that acupuncture for men both increases sperm production as well as improves the integrity of the sperm; for woman, acupuncture improves the uterine lining, increases blood flow to the uterus, helps to regulate hormone production, and reduces stress.

Biblical Commentaries on the Importance of Sex

The most famous Jewish scholar, Rambam (cited earlier), considered sex an inherent part of the relationship between husband and wife. When exploring his writings, some scholars note that he highlighted the specific section of the Talmud that speaks of "man's obligation" not just to have sex, but to satisfy his wife regularly and be responsive to her wishes. He authored many great books and treatises on numerous topics, from medicine to law, and he even wrote one treatise on sex and aphrodisiacs for the Sultan Omar (Rambam was his private physician).

Rabbi Joshua ben Levi goes even further by saying "Whoever compels his wife to have marital relations is unworthy of children." The rabbis and teachers of the day were sharing the view of the Torah and Talmud that making love is about showing respect toward one's wife. Moreover in the Talmud it says: "When you make love, you should have close bodily contact." This was highlighted because it was the most common practice of that era and beyond for people to have sex while fully clothed.

From the time of antiquity, the ancient Hebrews understood and interpreted human sexuality as a positive gift from God. They were not affected by the later Ancient Greek dualism between spirit and matter, which considered sexual intercourse an evil, "fleshy" activity, which was to be shunned and avoided if possible. Such thinking was foreign to the Hebrews, who saw sex within marriage as beautiful and enjoyable.

A wedding was a time of great celebration, partly because it marked the beginning of the sexual life of the couple. It is a romantic celebration of human sexuality. The bridal pair retired to a nuptial tent or chamber at the end of the wedding festivities to make love together while lying on a clean, white sheet. A newly betrothed man was even excused from participating in war in order to be able to enjoy his first weeks with his bride (Deuteronomy 20:7: "Let him depart and return to his house, otherwise he might die in the battle and another man would marry her.")!

Respect and Women's Rights

Perhaps one of the least discussed topics in the Bible and in the oral tradition of the Talmud encompasses the rights of a wife with respect to sex. The rabbis understood the importance of the wife's right to sex: The Talmud explains that a wife can compel her husband to have sex, but never the other way around (Talmud, Eiruvin 100b). The ancient rabbis went even further by explaining in the Talmud that it is the husband's obligation to ensure that his wife is sexually fulfilled.

Essentially, the reward of sex, in addition to the immediate pleasure it provides, is that of children, as it is said in Psalms 124:3: "Lo, children are a heritage of the Lord, the fruit of the womb is a reward." The Talmud is quite explicit in requiring a man to pleasure his wife first. Rabbi Hama, the son of the famed Rabbi Chanina, said, "As a reward for containing oneself during intercourse in order that one's wife may emit first, the Holy One blessed be He, gives one the reward of the fruit of the womb."

Monogamy

Genesis 2:24 reads: "A man shall leave his father and mother and hold fast to his wife, and they shall live as one flesh." Yet, later in Exodus 21:10, we find that God acknowledges that there are more women than men; in order for a woman to have protection and the beauty of having a child, she is permitted to marry a man with a wife or wives. "If he takes another wife, he will not diminish her food, clothing, or marital rights." However there is only a limited biblical period where plural marriages exist as with Abraham, Jacob, David, Moses, and Solomon. There was a reversal of this as stated in Deuteronomy 17:17: ". . . .and he shall not acquire many wives for himself, lest his heart will turn away, nor shall he acquire for himself excessive silver and gold." The later biblical texts and then the Talmud established that polygamy was forbidden and monogamy as the only permitted and sacred bond.

Evolving into God's Image

As we have stated at the outset of this chapter, the Book of Genesis was and is the logical starting point for our quest into the biblical view of sex. The first statement relating to human sexuality is found in Genesis 1:27: "So God created man in his own image, in the image of God He created him; male and female, He created them." It is noteworthy that while after every previous act of Creation, Scripture says that God saw "it was good" (see Genesis 1:12,

18, 21, 25), after the creation of humankind as male and female, it says that God saw "it was very good" (Genesis 1:31). This initial divine appraisal of human sexuality as "very good" shows that Scripture sees the male and female sexual distinction as part of the goodness and perfection of God's original creation.

Chapter 4

Ancient Healing Pathways

Universal Common Truths

There is vast overlap and resonance between all the major traditions, religions, and healing pathways. We have far more in common than anyone would believe. Yet throughout history from biblical times until today, humanity has focused on the differences. Too much blood has been spilled and continues to be spilled in these crazy times. So much hatred, violence and self-righteous bigotry is disseminated in the name of religion and culture. When one reads the texts from the Old Testament, New Testament, the Q'uran, Buddhist Tripitaka, the Vedic scriptures, and Confucius' Chinese four books and five classics, they all speak of love, harmony, and meaning. All our ancient pathways have a vast amount to say about healing, much of which is very similar.

We live in times in which we urgently require healing. We require healing for ourselves; our bodies and spirits, we require healing for the hatred and disharmony that exists and mostly we require healing for our planet.

Hebrew Medicine

The Old Testament abounds with medical wisdom that is shared throughout this manuscript. The first medical text in Hebrew is attributed to the 7th century physician Asaph Harofeh; His work was followed by the writings of the great Jewish physicians of Arabia in the ninth, tenth, and eleventh centuries. The most famous of 12th century Jewish physicians was Moses Maimonides, who was chief physician to the Sultan of Egypt. His text *Pirkei Moshe* taught of anatomy, physiology, pathology, gynecology, etiology of disease, diagnosis and therapeutics, surgery, hygiene, exercise, bathing, diet, drugs, and more. He also wrote books on hemorrhoids, seizures, cohabitation, asthma, and poisons and their antidotes. He is the author of a *materia medica* that details the flavors and temperatures of healing herbs, and an authoritative albeit brief treatise on diet and lifestyle (*Hanhagat Habriut*). He described four tastes (sweet, sharp, salty, and bitter) and discussed their specific qualities in healing products and foods.

Although not as complex, this is distinctly similar to the systems of traditional Chinese medicine (TCM). Maimonides was so revered as a physician and healer that his legend persists in the Arab world to this day. Maimonides was also a revered Jewish scholar and leader of the Jewish community far beyond Egypt. Referred to as Rambam (a contracted form of Rabbi Moses ben Maimon), he produced extensive commentaries on Jewish law and ethics that continue to influence modern Jews. The Jewish medical tradition has thrived wherever Jewish culture has flourished.

Love thy Neighbor: A Dream of Harmony and Peace

One of the most famous rabbis (teachers), Rabbi Akiva of the first century, was famous for saying, "You should love thy neighbor as thyself," as is taught in Leviticus 19:18. Later, a similar famous disciple, Hillel, was asked to teach the entire Torah (Bible) while standing on one foot. He replied, "What you hate done to you, do not do unto others; this is the entire Torah, and the rest is commentary; now go and learn it."

The most well-known ethical similarities among spiritual and ethical systems and religions is the "The Golden Rule"—cited both by Hillel in Judaism and Confucius. It is understood to be good deeds in prudence with words and love of man.

From Moses to Jesus to Confucius to Mohammed, every major faith has taught similar principles. Matthew 7:12 reads: "In everything, therefore, treat people the same way you want them to treat you, for this is the Law and the Prophets." The Koran states: "The most righteous of men is the one who is glad that men should have what is pleasing to him, and who dislikes for them what is for him disagreeable" (Qur'an, Surah 59, 83). Ghandi said, "The true measure of any society can be found in how it treats its most vulnerable members," which goes back to ancient Greece.

Imagine if children of all denominations worldwide—Buddhist, Christian, Hindu, Jewish, Moslem—could all just learn this one common value from all their wisdoms?

Confucius did qualify that the fulfillment of "love men" as in Judaism's "love thy neighbor" is not limited to a family, a clan, a tribe, a city or a country: it is extended to all human beings. However, Confucius's dispensation of love has priorities, beginning with the directive that one should love one's parent's first, as expressed in the Fifth Commandment in the Two Tablets: "Honor thy father and thy mother; then other family members; then one's villagers; then countrymen; then others."

Respect for all Human Life

The Bible has much to say about respecting human life. In Samuel 16:7, The Lord said to Samuel, "Do not look on his appearance or on the height of his stature, because I have rejected him. For the Lord sees not as man sees; man looks on the outward appearance, but the Lord looks on the heart." This is central to the Bible. Respect for the internal authentic self is something central to all pathways.

Where have we lost the way? How many of us actually heard this from our parents and have shared it with our children? Dr. Martin Luther King said it best: "I have a dream that my four little children will one day live in a nation where they will not be judged by the color of their skin but by the content of their character."

We are all from the same DNA

As we survive as a species, we recognize that all of us are derived from the same original DNA. It does not matter whether you believe it came from Adam and Eve in the Bible or from the scientific version of a mitochondrial Eve and mitochondrial Adam, as discovered by Allan Wilson and his doctoral students (Cann, Stoneking) who showed a direct genetic link between most of us on this planet and an ancestor who lived 140,000 to 200,000 years ago somewhere in East Africa.

Enlightenment

In Buddhism, to be "enlightened" means to see others as themselves, not to judge. This is true at the core of all the great belief systems. So why did we as a global society fail so miserably after thousands of years of teachings and warnings? The tragedy is that historical wars—and more so current world events and terrorism—are often perpetrated in the name of religion. If we genuinely and honestly embraced some basic tenets from the Bible and ancient religious texts, perhaps it would allow us to live in a more civilized manner. The reality is that we are all in this together. There is a commonly held belief that when we reach a critical mass of enough enlightened and good people in the world, we can really begin to make a difference.

Buddhism and Judaism: A Brief Comparison

Buddhism started in India at about 5th century B.C.E. and began its spread through Asia from about the 3rd century B.C.E. when King Asoka sent out missionaries to South Asia and to the West. In the course of time, it evolved into two major traditions, known in ancient times as Hinayana and Mahayana, the Smaller and the Larger Vehicles. Buddhism is sometimes described as a philosophy in search of a religion.

The consequence of this difference has been that Buddhism focuses on certain philosophic principles rather than beliefs. There are beliefs, but they are not the primary consideration. Buddhism

is an optimistic system and proposes a cure or healing: Whatever
has a cause can be remedied by removing the cause. From the
beginning, the Buddha realized that just as one can suffer from
physical disease, one could also suffer from an unhealthy mindset.
The Buddha's medicine treats disease by starting with the patient's
mind, curing him of the three poisons—greed, hate, and igno-
rance. According to Buddhism, the pure and wondrous dharma,
the principles of divine law, is the perfect medication for an ailing
mind, as well as for a sick body.

In Judaism, the Bible follows the same thought: "A joyful heart
is good medicine, but a crushed spirit dries up the bone" (Proverbs 17:22). The ability to cope with life's stresses is a skill. It is
something that can be lost and learned. The Bible teaches the idea
that, while there are many ways to learn to cope with stress, the
most powerful is belief in God. Belief and faith in the Lord is the
place one needs to turn to learn how to cope with stress, because
God delivers that help each and every day: "I will lift up my eyes to
the mountains; from whence shall my help come? My help comes
from the Lord, Who made heaven and earth" (Psalms 121:12).

Judaic and Buddhist ideas of death and rebirth bear some similarities, too. This may go back beyond Vedanta, even to similarities
in the biographies of Moses and the Buddha: born to or raised
by royal families, they took radical steps to break free from their
physical and theological confinements—Moses by plunging into
the world, the Buddha by retreating from it.

In Judaism, history is part of the moment—this moment, every moment. History is the unfolding of redemption. Events are
foretold in prophecy and in history, moving toward an ultimate
ingathering. In Mahayana Buddhism, for example, this moment is
this moment. Every moment simply is, and it does not bear with it
the lengthening or crushing train of historical precedent. Judaism
is a religion of prophets, with many of the central figures of the
Scriptures experiencing direct contact with God. In Christianity,
too, God graces all of the holy Saints. However, Confucius is considered as a prophet-philosopher in the sense that he received Dao

and taught it to his students; and he received the Dao by learning, rather than by divine revelation.

Buddhism, Chinese, and Western Medicine

In the sutras, the discourses of the Buddha that constitute the basic text of Buddhist scriptures, we can find analogies that describe the Buddha as the doctor, and knowledge of the dharma as the medicine; monastics serve as the nursing staff, and all people as the patients. According to this medical analogy, Buddhism is considered a medication with a broad meaning—a medication that can cure the ailments in all aspects of life. In general, Western medicine functions within a much smaller framework. Western medicine typically approaches illness through physical symptoms. This approach tends to temporarily reduce the suffering and remove the symptoms for a period, but a lack of symptoms does not mean that the root cause has been identified and removed. Therefore, the complete elimination of the disease has not occurred.

Buddhism—as does Judaism—offers patients not only symptomatic relief, but also spiritual guidance to ensure overall and long-lasting health. This is often shared in the works of Maimonides and the Chassidic teachings particularly those of Rabbi Nachman of Breslov in Ukraine.

In the East, religion has impacted the field of health and medicine for a much longer time. Eastern medical practitioners never doubted the role of religion in disease; the two have been integrated for thousands of years. Out of thousands of documents in the Tripitaka ("Three Baskets"—a term that originally referred to three receptacles containing the scrolls on which the Buddhist scriptures were originally preserved), a significant number contain records about Buddhist medicine. When this canon of discourses and sutras was brought to China, the most salient aspects of Indian Buddhism blended with the most highly regarded aspects of Chinese medicine. Through modifications and improvements contributed by numerous Buddhist masters from the past and present, the Chinese Buddhist medical system evolved into the one that presently exists.

The Buddha as the Great Doctor and Maimonides

Buddha was capable of curing diseases, not only of the body but also of the mind, and these were his specialty. In the sutra of Buddha's Diagnosis, the Buddha explained that a doctor should progress through four steps when helping a patient. Doctors must: (1) discover the origin of the illness; (2) achieve a thorough understanding of the illness; (3) prescribe the appropriate medication to cure the illness; and (4) completely cure the illness in a manner that prevents it from reoccurring. In addition to mastering these four criteria, a good doctor should always act with a generous heart when treating patients, considering them as his or her dearest friends.

Lastly, the Buddha recommended that the doctor offer advice to patients in order to help them heal quickly and thoroughly. He recommended that patients: (1) be cautious and selective about the food they eat; (2) consume food at the proper intervals; (3) stay in touch with their doctors and nurses, always acting kindly and graciously towards them; (4) keep an optimistic or hopeful outlook; and (5) be kind and considerate of those who are caring for them. The Buddha believed that a cooperative effort from the doctors, caretakers, and patients yielded the best results from treatment. The Buddha was not just an average doctor; he was an exceptional doctor who had vision and insight. The principles on self-preservation recommended by Dr. Moses Ben Maimom (or Maimonides) that offered directives on, how and what to eat and on healing are almost identical to these outlined here by Buddha.

Repentance and Confession

Confession is another practice that helps to restore and maintain our health: It is like clean water that washes away the dirt from one's heart and the dust from one's mind. A Buddhist story about a Tang Master named Wuda offers us an example of how confession can be a healing agent. Master Wuda had a man killed in a previous life. Seeking revenge in future lives, the man who was killed was reborn as a sore on Master Wuda's foot. No doctor could cure the sore because it was a manifestation of Master Wuda's bad karma. After seeking guidance from an Arhat, who helped him to realize his wrongdoing, Master Wuda repented with a sincere heart, cleansed his wound with pure water, and the sore disappeared. Only the heart of repentance could cure Master Wuda of his ailment. Thus, Buddhists repent mistakes and misdeeds to the Buddha and vow not to repeat the same behavior and create more bad karma.

In addition, with the heart and mind of a bodhisattva (an enlightened one being full of compassion), one may compassionately repent for all beings, thereby relieving their suffering as well as one's own. Psychologically, repentance is believed to release impure thoughts and worrisome guilt that act like toxins in our bodies. It alleviates our mental burdens and reduces the potential for illness. Repentance is a central tenet within Hebraic tradition and Confession is a basic component of Christian religions.

Christian Healing

Healing and well-being of body, mind, and spirit are central tenets of Christian faith of all denominations. Jesus was often referred to as Christ the physician (Christus medicus), by which he was to be understood as relieving the soul's as well as the body's burdens. Christianity brought comfort, compassion, and care to the sick and injured. Throughout history, religion and spirituality and the practice of medicine have been intertwined. As a result, many religions embrace a caring for the sick as a primary mission, and many of the world's leading medical institutions have religious and spiritual roots.

Recently, a Mayo clinic academic review of 1200 valid clinical studies that have used religious and spiritual variables in assessing health was conducted. This body of research demonstrates that religious involvement and spirituality are associated with better health outcomes. The mechanisms by which religious involvement and spirituality affect health are not always understood; they undoubtedly involve complex interactions of psychosocial and behavioral factors on biological processes as well as immeasurables such as belief and the supernatural.

The studies have also shown that religious involvement and spirituality are associated with greater longevity, better coping skills, and much improved health-related quality of life, and they demonstrate less anxiety, depression, and suicide. Most importantly, several studies indicate that addressing the spiritual needs of the patient may enhance recovery from illness. Prayer even works for agnostics, as the body possesses a physiological response to the repetition of a phrase or action.

Indigenous Aboriginal Culture and Healing

The healing and natural traditions of Indigenous Australians are also aligned with Buddhist views. Anne Warren, an Aboriginal elder and medicine woman, explains, "In traditional Aboriginal medicine, which is entirely holistic and preventive, 'spirit' is the ultimate wisdom. If the spirit is well, the body will be well. So we heal the spirit through the body." Traditional healing is very close to what today is labeled the Eastern healing approach. "You don't address one part of the body without healing the whole body," Warren adds. Connecting to spirit has a lot to do with deep listening: "Spirit comes in through dreams, visions, signs, and symbols in our daily lives," she says. "It's about listening to everything, acknowledging the interconnectedness between yourself and every living thing."

For example, if someone has a pain in the stomach, the center of digestion, it might help to ask, "What are you not digesting?" If a woman is suffering period pain, she should ask about the creative outlet she need, as a woman's reproductive organs are the center of feminine creativity. In Aboriginal traditional healing, Warren says, "every plant, too, has a spiritual aspect that must be taken into account."

Three Body Types, Four Elements, Six Realms, Ten Emanations

According to Buddhism, the body is composed of four impermanent elements—earth, water, fire, and wind. Judaism's mystical writings called Kabbala and Ayurvedic medicine (ancient Indian) also speak frequently of four elements. Ayurveda speaks of three body types: Kapha, Pitta, and Vata that describe our natures, inclinations, and how best to balance them.

In Kabbala we have the tree of life representing the human body's energies that correspond to the ten emanations of God's energies. In Buddhism, consciousness is reborn in one of the six realms, which are basically six realms of existence based on karma and on one's moralistic behavior. This theory is the foundation of Indian Buddhist medical science. Chinese medicine, an extension of Buddhism, with its emphasis on living in a tranquil state, which reduces stress and protects the body, believes the body is comprised of a unique system of subsidiary channels that transmits vital energy (chi), blood, nutrients, and other substances through the five organs and six internal regions in one's body. In all these ancient systems, the occurrence of a disease is closely related to one's mental health, physical health, spiritual health, behavior, habits, living environment, and even the society and culture in which one lives. Harmonizing all these elements and engaging in specific practices can help to bring about optimum health and prevent illness. Gaining awareness about the cause of illness and conducting our lives in a manner that nourishes and maintains long-term good health can drastically improve our overall well-being. A good doctor is well-learned in prescribing the right food and medicine to adjust the four elements and nourish a patient's body during a particular season. When this intricate circulation system is flowing properly, the four elements stay in balance, the major organs can perform their essential functions, and the body remains healthy. These precepts are the basis of contemporary Preventive Health as discussed previously.

Imbalance of the Four Elements

In 450 B.C.E., Hippocrates, the father of medicine presented the theory that all human ailments are caused by an imbalance of the "four humours": black bile, yellow bile, phlegm, and blood. These corresponded to the four basic personality types: sanguine (courageous); choleric (bad tempered); melancholic (despondent); and phlegmatic (unemotional). Japanese practices utilize blood types to determine if one is compatible in a certain work environment. Type A is cooperative, smart pleasant, and sensitive, but can't handle stress as well as other blood types— with stress, his immune system is weakened; Type B is more balanced, very ambitious, and more prone to certain autoimmune disease; type AB is charming, easygoing, and found in only 2 to 5 percent of the population; type O individuals are either loners or leaders, more self-reliant, muscular, and able to handle stress more readily.

The third volume of *Nanhai Ji Gui Neifa Zhu* (a record of Buddhist practices) states: "If diseases are related to the four elements, they are usually caused by overeating or overexertion." An imbalance of the four elements and the resulting illness can also occur due to a diet that is not in tune with the four seasons. When the seasons change and the temperature varies from cool to cold, to warm to hot, it is important to adjust our diet in a manner that enables the body to function at its best. In the Suvarnaprabhasottama Sutra, a young man asked his father who was a doctor, "How do we cure the suffering of human beings and cure diseases that arise from the imbalance of the four elements?" The doctor responded to his son by saying, "We live our lives through four seasons of three months, or six seasons of two months in some parts of the world. Whether four or six, we must live according to the seasons, eating food that corresponds with hot and cold, warm, and cool. In this way, our bodies will benefit; when the season and the food are in balance, so too will the body be in balance." This is closely aligned with aboriginal philosophy, which is lived through six distinct seasons.

Chinese Medicine: Acupuncture, Medicinals, and Energy

Two schools of thought led to the development of various methods of Chinese medicine. One has contributed to the development of medicinal plants and acupuncture methods. The second led to the perception-based control circuit and input circuit in which certain organs have hierarchical priority over others. These methods developed deep philosophical concepts that became part of Chinese medicine.

The Chinese were studying medicine long before the West. Traditional Chinese Medicine (TCM) was founded by Fu Xi—who introduced the use of nine needles—about 8,000 years ago; about 5,000 years ago, Sheng Nong studied and shared herbal medicine and tested toxic substances on himself, perhaps identifying 365 herbs that had some form of medicinal property. Later, in the Zhou dynasty (1100-221 B.C.E.), meridians were being used for the art of acupuncture and the concept of "yin and yang" was incorporated. Hua To was using anesthetics to treat patients during surgery 1,500 years before the West. In addition, the oldest known medical text book was written by Hung-Di Nei-Jing between 800–200 B.C.E.

In studying Chinese medicine, we see that the actual use of acupuncture can be traced back 3,500 years. The general premise of acupuncture is that the body contains patterns of energy flow known as "qi," and that this flow of qi is necessary to help maintain homeostasis within the body. According to the theory of acupuncture, there are more than 2,000 points on the human body that connect with 20 pathways (meridians). These pathways conduct the qi throughout the body. For the past fifteen years, Dr. Kash has utilized acupuncture to treat his own pain from spinal surgery when strong painkillers were ineffective. The use of acupuncture also serendipitously treated his fertility quagmire caused by the fact he'd had the mumps as a child.

Many pain centers around the world today, in addition in to China and Japan, have acupuncturists on staff; some of the leading fertility centers also employ licensed acupuncturists. Acupuncture was re-introduced to the West by former U.S. Secretary of State Dr. Henry Kissinger. In 1972, he traveled to China along with James Reston, a journalist for the *New York Times*. While in China, Mr. Reston fell ill and ended up in a Chinese hospital, requiring an emergency appendectomy. To relieve his pain, doctors used acupuncture, and Dr. Kissinger witnessed the procedure. Today, many doctors recommend acupuncture for a variety of health issues including pain.

Pulse Points: Jewish Kabbalah, Ayurveda, and Traditional Chinese Medicine

In the mystical Jewish tradition of the *Kabbalah*, there are ten main pulse patterns that are used to detect physiological as well as spiritual imbalances; each pulse pattern indicates a specific vital energy that flows into the body via the soul. *Ayurveda*, a holistic medical pathway originating in India, describes in detail the use of pulse patterns to diagnose disease. In TCM (*Traditional Chinese Medicine*) the use of pulse detection is also vital in the diagnosis of disease. It is based on three paired pulse points on each wrist and 18 diagnostic positions that are used to define 28 different pulse patterns.

All three traditions— Hebrew, Ayurvedic, and Buddhist— emphasize function over structure, and harmony of spiritual energy. They also share a belief that happiness, and even pleasure, are essential to a happy heart and soul, and a clear mind.

Additional similarities between TCM and Judaism can be found in Jewish Scriptures. In the Talmud for example, the rabbis address the different functions of the organs from a metaphysical perspective. They teach that the two kidneys influence a person's thought processes by challenging them to rethink what might otherwise be uninhibited thinking and reacting. They are the seat of the individual's deepest inclinations and attitudes. In addition to the intellectual influence of the kidneys, they also noted that the heart understands; it is the source of conscious emotions, such as fear and love. The lungs draw up different liquids, the trachea produces sound, the mouth and lips express what the tongue articulates, the esophagus takes and expels food, the liver gets angry, the spleen causes laughter, the gall bladder secretes bile to soothe the liver's anger, the stomach causes sleep, and the nose wakes up.

Judaism and Confucianism: Where did they Intersect?

Is it possible that the Israelites were in China at the time of Confucius? The evidence is overwhelming that the ancient northern Hebrew tribes migrated to Jeddah (today a port city in modern Saudi Arabia), and on to India, and then China. There is even some evidence of Jews' settling in Japan. King Solomon had a massive and vast navy for ancient times; hence, there had to be seafaring navigators among the ancient Israelites. Confucius lived approximately 2,500 years ago, during the same period when the Babylonians conquered Israel, about 586 B.C.E. There is enough supporting evidence that the ancient Hebrews traveled to Saudi Arabia, and many eventually were absorbed into Islam; others traveled to India and what is today called Kashmir; then to China to what is known as the Szechuan region.

The historical traveling routes of the ancient Hebrews date back to around the Han Dynasty, about 206 B.C.E. Almost one thousand years later, in the Xinjing northern province, the first European Jew to write on his findings in China was a merchant by the name of Jacob d'Ancona. In 1270, he traveled from Italy to China and found evidence of a large community of Jews in the Guanzhiu or central region. Not too many years later, Marco Polo witnessed evidence of Chinese Jews: Jews had been living in Kaifeng since the Northern Song Dynasty (960–1127), which, at the time, was the capital of the Chinese empire due to the Silk Road, and was the most populated city on the planet.

Thus, for nearly 2,500 years, there has been a Jewish/Hebrew presence in China; it continues to this very day. During World War II, both China and Japan took in Jewish refugees from Europe, and there was, and still is, virtually no discrimination whatsoever. We know that years later (1368–1644), the original Ming emperor conferred on the Jews seven surnames: Ai, Lao, Jin, Li, Shi, Zhang, and Zhao. Chinese Jews will almost always have one of these seven names.

Judaism, and especially the rabbinic tradition, includes some philosophical statements that are remarkably consistent with Eastern philosophy. The concept that "Everything is in the hands of Heaven but the fear of Heaven" (Talmud) is very consistent with Confucianism, both in thought and in terminology. The Confucian *li* (the way or correct conduct) and Judaism's halachah (law or way) have many striking similarities. Confucius: "What you do not want done to yourself, do not do to others." Hillel the sage: "What is hateful to you, do not do to your neighbor."

The Bible, God's inspired work to Moses, had many stories of various biblical figures. The intention of the biblical stories was not to glorify the figures but to convey the message to all Jews. In ancient China, many writers wrote numerous writings under the name of the philosopher Confucius. They thought that if their writings were attributed to Confucius, the public would then accept them as superior. The goal was to share an inherent philosophy, a way of life. So, too, most Buddhist lessons come from the Buddha. These are the primordial figures from which the truth emanates.

Disease is not Divine Punishment

The original Mosaic and Abrahamic texts are clear in the fact that disease is definitely not a divine punishment. Undoubtedly some errant beliefs creep into cultural systems over thousands of years. The biblical Hebrews may have inherited a number of beliefs from ancient Mesopotamian cultures, among them a conviction that disease was divine punishment and therefore a mark of sin. This belief was passed on as a basic concept to Christian medieval Europe. Assyro-Babylonian taboos against close proximity to the sick were also continued by the Hebrews in their isolation of the unclean, who, in addition to the diseased, included the dead, a potential source of soul transference among the Mesopotamian peoples. If one explores deeply into the mystical text, it is clear that disease is not punishment.

Restoration and Healing from Disease

Restoration from disease is described in almost all sacred texts. Much is written over centuries about remarkable faith healing by Holy Christian Saints, beginning of course with Jesus Christ. Healing may come from realigning yin and yang or developing more chi. Or, in contemporary society, we require the integration of the best of modern medicine together with healthy lifestyle interventions and adjunct therapies such as meditation, mindfulness, acupuncture, and the like. Yet faith and prayer still play a significant role in most pathways. God (by whatever name and described in whichever way) is the great healer:

—"Who forgiveth all thine iniquities; who heals all thy diseases" (Psalms 103:3);

—"But unto you that fear my name shall the sun of righteousness arise with healing in his wings" (Malachi 4:2);

—"I am the Lord that healeth thee" (Exodus 15:26);

—"My son, forget not My law; but let thine heart keep My commandments: For length of days and long life and peace, shall they add to thee" (Proverbs 3:1-2).

Chapter 5

Joy and Laughter;
Pain and Suffering

Laughter and Pain

Laughter in the Bible is often described in contrast to painful situations. In Psalms 126:2, we find a description of former captives who, upon being released, were returning to their homes, filled with mirth: "Our mouths were filled with laughter, our tongues with songs of joy." What a simple but eloquent description of their happiness after the fear and pain of captivity.

In Scriptures, laughter is mainly juxtaposed with pain:

—"Even in laughter, the heart may ache, and joy may end in grief" (Proverbs 14:13);

—"He will yet fill your mouth with laughter and your lips with shouts of joy" (Job 8:21);

—"A time to weep and a time to laugh, a time to mourn and a time to dance" (Ecclesiastes 3:4).

The Best Medicine

So what does the Bible say about laughter? It is first mentioned in Genesis. Both Abraham and Sarah are caught laughing when God promises them a child in their old age. Abraham fell face down; he laughed and said to himself, "Will a son be born to a man a hundred years old? Will Sarah bear a child at the age of ninety?" Sarah was listening at the entrance to the tent, which was behind him. Abraham and Sarah were already old and well advanced in years, and Sarah was past the age of child bearing. So Sarah laughed to herself as well, and thought, "After I am worn out and my master is old, will I now have this pleasure?" This particular laughter was not only a response to the irony of the situation, but it was also rooted in pain, because both Abraham and Sarah had long hoped and prayed for a child. I suppose they laughed so they wouldn't cry. She named her son Yitzchak, in which the root of the Hebrew word for laughter can be found.

A Treatment for Pain?

In *Anatomy of an Illness: As Perceived by the Patient*, Norman Cousins, a political journalist, author and professor of Medical Humanities at UCLA, tells of being hospitalized with a rare, crippling disease. When he was told his condition was incurable, Cousins checked out of the hospital. Aware of the harmful effects that negative emotions can have on the body, he reasoned that the reverse must also be true. So, he borrowed a movie projector and prescribed his own treatment: liberal doses of Marx Brothers films and old *Candid Camera* reruns. It didn't take long for him to discover that just ten minutes of laughter provided him with two hours of pain-free sleep. Amazingly, his debilitating disease was eventually reversed.

After the account of his victory appeared in the *New England Journal of Medicine*, Cousins received more than 3,000 letters from appreciative physicians throughout the world. In his book *Head First: The Biology of Hope and the Healing Power of the Human Spirit* (New York: Penguin Books, 1990), Cousins describes a survey of 649 oncologists, of which 90 percent of them said that they place the highest value on the attitudes of hope and optimism for a patient's ability to deal with life-threatening illness.

Even as far back as 1928, Dr. James Walsh wrote the book *Laughter and Health* (New York: D. Appleton & Co., 1928), in which he provided evidence that laughter lowered pain in post-surgery patients. Today much mainstream research has documented the healing power of laughter and joy on pain and health outcomes.

The efficacy of laughter, as a method of pain control, can be attributed to several things, as previously suggested: it reduces muscle tension, distracts attention from the pain, has a positive effect on a person's attitude, and can actually stimulate the release of endorphins, the body's natural painkillers. In addition, laughter stimulates the cardiovascular system, thereby increasing oxygenation of the blood, which further promotes healing.

In the fast-paced twenty-first century— a time of turmoil, terrorism, job uncertainty, a sharp rise in the crime rate, and a phenomenally widespread societal use of drugs and alcohol—a good sense of humor is a most valuable commodity.

Jewish Humor: A Vaccine against Suffering

Jewish humor has been referred to as "laughter with a tear in the middle." Millenia of tragedy, hardship, pogroms, holocausts, dispersion, and deep pain has always been accompanied by a sharp sense of humor. Very often it is a bittersweet humor, but laughter and the pursuit of joy is central in Mosaic tradition.

(So it makes perfect sense that the "People of the Book," gave the world so many "Comedians of the Book": Milton Berle, Mel Brooks, Al Jolson, Henny Youngman, Phil Silvers, Don Rickles, Freddie Roman, Adam Sandler, Jerry Seinfeld, Jack Black, Joan Rivers, Gene Wilder, Allan Sherman, Red Buttons, Victor Borge, Woody Allen, Jon Stewart, Larry David, Robert Klein, Jerry Lewis, Billy Crystal, Jerry Stiller, Ben Stiller, George Burns, Gary Shandling, David Brenner, Gabe Kaplan, Goldie Hawn, Gilda Radner, Danny Kaye, Myron Cohen, Harold Ramis, Paul Reiser, Fran Drescher, Alan King, Albert Brooks, Buddy Hackett, Carl Reiner, Paul Reiser, Totie Fields, the Marx Brothers, Sacha Cohen, Peter

Sellers, Jackie Mason, Rodney Dangerfield, and, of course, the Three Stooges.)

Perhaps the disproportionate number of Jewish comedians is a direct correlation to the disproportionate number of catastrophes over the millennia; without laughter all hope would be lost. Laughter was always pain medicine. Humor in Jewish theology and culture is possibly a metaphoric "vaccine" against pain and suffering.

Health Outcomes of Humor and Laughter

Proverbs 17:22 reads: "A joyful heart is good medicine, but a crushing spirit dries up the bones." One cannot imagine getting through the difficulties of life without the comfort of humor. Biblical scholars tell us that it can be found in even the most desperate of situations.

There is evidence that humor can decrease stress, diminish pain, and enhance quality of life. There have even been some data correlating laughter with an enhancement of immune function.

Consider some of the physical benefits of laughing:

—Laughter lowers the levels of cortisol in our body; cortisol suppresses our immune system;

—Laughter causes endorphins to be released into the body with the same exhilarating effect as doing strenuous exercise;

—Laughter stimulates our hearts and lungs and improves our breathing capacity;

—Laughing for only 15 minutes yields the same benefit as 2 hours of sleep;

—The link between laughter and blood vessels was first reported in 2005 by researchers at the University of Maryland Medical Center. The findings revealed that laughter causes the dilatation of the endothelium—the inner lining of blood vessels—and increases blood flow.

Over the past few decades beginning in 1971 when Dr. Hunter Doherty (Patch Adams) set up the revolutionary Gesundheit Institute, many hospitals have implemented laughter therapy programs for both children and adult patients in the form of "comedy carts" or doctor–clowns to bring some laughter and joy into a patient's painful hospital experience.

The Science of Humor
From a psychological perspective, humor involves cognitive, emotional, behavioral, psycho-physiological, and social aspects. The term humor can refer to a stimulus, which is intended to produce a humorous response (such as a humorous video), a mental process (perception of amusing moments in time), or a response (laughter, exhilaration). Just watch a Three Stooges film or an episode of *The Nanny* in any of the dozens of different languages around the world. Watch *The Wedding Crashers* or *Seinfeld* on an airplane, and hear the laughter throughout the plane. Laughter is the most common expression of a humorous experience. Humor and laughter are also typically associated with a pleasant emotional state. In Job 8:21, we read: "He will fill your mouth with laughter, and your lips with shouting."

Joy and Laughter throughout History
It may be that the effects of joyful activities and laughter work by reducing the effects of stress. The fourteenth-century French surgeon Henri de Mondeville wrote: "Let the surgeon take care to regulate the regime of the patient for joy and happiness, allowing his relatives and friends to cheer him up by sharing jokes." Since then, numerous clinicians have shared anecdotal data concerning the development of illness in persons with certain psychological styles, or after a stressful life event, such as bereavement. In addition to the experience of author Norman Cousins, as noted ear-

lier, there is a great deal of evidence from a variety of studies that laughter, and even simple hugging, helps boosts the immune system. The thoughts of other notables are cited below:

—"The most wasted of days is one without laughter." **Poet E. E. Cummings**

—"Those who don't know how to weep with their heart don't know how to laugh either." **Golda Meir**

—"Laughter is the shortest distance between two people." **Victor Borge**

—"It is cheerful to God when you rejoice or laugh from the bottom of your heart." **Martin Luther King, Jr.**

—"The human race has only one really effective weapon, and this is laughter." **Mark Twain**

A Neurological Approach to Laughter and Joy
Some preliminary studies have examined the neurological processes involved in the effects of laughter on stress and immune functioning. The complex field of neuroscience has advanced dramatically particularly since the advent of PET (Positron Emission Tomography) scans which have allowed scientists to peek into the functioning brain. As yet there is still much we don't know especially about how the brain functions in response to humor and joy.

Laughter is not uniquely human but present in other mammals too. Neurobiologists and psychologist Professor Robert Provine from the University of Maryland demonstrated that chimpanzees have similar laughing sound patterns to those of humans.

But while there is considerable information on the neuronal representation of speech, much less is known about brain mechanisms of laughter. Specific regions in the brain have been examined using electric current that stimulates laughter. The data suggest that there are different anatomical locations for the neurological response to humorous stimuli. However, more research is needed to determine how these neurological changes subsequently affect the physiological response to stressors and possibly improve immune functioning.

Communication is What it's All About

One way in which we, as humans, are truly separated from other animal species is through our ability to communicate the way we do, although the evidence is indisputable that other highly developed mammals, such as dolphins, elephants, and wolves, may communicate through certain pitches and frequency vibrations emitted by their vocal cords. Other primates may have distinct sounds for expressing certain emotions or warnings such as laughter and joy. But the development of the hyoid bone, between the chin and throat, allows human beings to have a wide range of vocabulary.

In addition, the part of the cerebral cortex of the brain known as Wernicke's area—through which words and syllables are written and pronounced—is just as important as Broca's region of the brain, which is responsible for speech. Anthropologists and archeologists can debate when speech became inherent; but there seems to be a consensus of opinion that about 100,000 years ago, homo sapiens were able to communicate with language skill sets, although it may have developed even farther back.

The FOXP2 gene, which is indigenous to humans, had a direct role in the ability of human beings to communicate through speech. The evidence is solid that humans and their predecessors from as far back as 200,000 years ago occupied the Kebara Caves in Haifa; Neanderthal skeletons show that as far back as 60,000 years ago, they had an intact hyoid bone. DNA has shown that they had the FOXP2 gene as well, thereby leading to the presumption that they had the ability to communicate with a language. And if there was language, there had to be laughter; perhaps the DNA of one of these cave dwellers was passed on to the first great-great-grandparents of all the Jewish comedians.

Inappropriate Humor and Embarrassment

There are times when humor can be inappropriate and counterproductive. Human beings seem to have a great capacity for turning a tool into a weapon. This holds true with humor, too. Laughing at and embarrassing someone is especially harmful. The Rabbis of the Talmud (written commentaries of the Bible) were so opposed to public embarrassment that the famous Rabbi Yonah stated, "One who humiliates another person in front of others, goes to (Hell) and does not return."

Embarrassing someone is considered a "type of death." The emphatic tone was obviously to let us mere mortals understand the importance of not hurting others, not just physically but verbally as well. Bullying is at an all-time high worldwide. According to one global study of 500,000 students, almost 20 percent of students reported getting bullied regularly, and cyberbullying continues to rise.

While a healthy sense of humor can relieve tension and restore perspective, there are other forms of "humor," such as "put-downs," hurtful comments, and inappropriate jokes that insult and can be painful to the point of devastation for the one who is the brunt of this behavior.

Pain and Pain Syndromes

As humans we deal with physical pain, almost on a daily basis. This is nature's not very subtle way of telling us that we should stop doing what we are doing or that we have injured ourselves. Things like headaches, back pain, and arthritis are extremely common, and physical trauma, degenerative conditions, pain after surgery or from illnesses such as cancer are common, too. Thankfully, there is pain relief in the form of numerous therapeutic approaches including medications.

We also deal with an enormous amount emotional pain and suffering through life through loss, bereavement, and life's trials and tribulations. Depression and anxiety, although not new, is greater than ever and relieving emotional pain is often much more complex.

Acute pain from an injury or illness is usually well controlled by medications and often resolves the problem. Chronic pain is defined as pain lasting longer than three to six months and is due to a multitude of musculoskeletal and other physical causes. It is commonly associated with other illness as well as higher rates of depression and anxiety.

Chronic Pain Syndromes (CPS) are extremely common and a major challenge due to the complex nature and poor response to traditional therapies. Many of them fall into categories such as Fibromyalgia, which affects millions of individuals worldwide with symptoms that include chronic fatigue, joint pain, tiredness, and anxiety.

Pain Killers in the Bible

Today we have an abundance of choices of pain-killer medications including non-steroidal anti-inflammatory agents, paracetamol, aspirin, acetaminophen, as well as the opiate derivatives. One of the best ways of dealing with pain in relatively modern medicine was originally acetylsalicylic acid, better known as aspirin. Science did not begin to fully understand the value of this true miracle drug for treating fever, headaches, pain, and cardiac issues until the 1960s.

The Egyptians were using some form of salicylate, derived from Ebers papyrus, as far back as 1543 B.C.E.; the Romans used willow extracts as a source for salicylates as well. It was being used some 1,970 years ago for treating: redness, heat, swelling, and pain. Even Hippocrates referred to using salicylic tea to reduce fevers 2,400 years ago; and the Chinese used white willow as an anti-inflammatory 2,500 years ago.

The Bible goes back even further. Ezekiel 17:4-6 says: "He broke off the topmost of its young twigs and carried it to a land of trade and set it in a city of merchants. Then he took of the seed of the land and planted it in fertile soil. He placed it beside abundant waters. He set it like a willow twig, and it sprouted and became a low spreading vine, and its branches turned toward him, and its roots remained where it stood. So it became a vine and produced branches and put out boughs."

Some commentaries actually explain the medicinal use of white willow, as in Psalms 137:1-9: "By the waters of Babylon, there we sat down and wept, when we remembered Zion. On the willows, there we hung up our lyres. For there our captors required of us songs, and our tormentors, mirth, saying, 'Sing us one of the songs of Zion!' How shall we sing the Lord's song in a foreign land? If I forget you, O Jerusalem, let my right hand forget its skill." And Leviticus 23:40 reads: "And you shall take on the first day the fruit of splendid trees, branches of palm trees and boughs of leafy trees and willows of the brook, and you shall rejoice before the Lord your God seven days."

Chapter 6

Preventive Medicine
in the Bible

A Worldwide Crisis

Healthcare issues are clearly among the most critical problems facing the world today. National health-care costs have been soaring in all countries and are projected to continue to increase in the next 10 years. Millions of people globally lack adequate health insurance. In spite of billions of dollars spent on medical research, much still remains unknown about many diseases. The chronic diseases of lifestyle—which are mainly due to our poor lifestyle choices such as smoking, alcohol consumption, sedentary behavior, bad nutrition, and overwhelming stress—continue to soar. We are facing a massive epidemic of obesity, diabetes, cardiovascular diseases, and cancers.

Although Contemporary Western Medicine has, for the most part, focused on the treatment of diseases, rather than on their prevention, the paradigm has shifted and is continuing to shift towards a much greater focus on our own personal involvement and the prevention of illness.

Take Personal Responsibility

It should not be assumed that the Bible places the entire responsibility of maintaining good health on physicians. In fact, most biblical interpreters stated that the major responsibility falls on the individual. This philosophy is totally aligned with the contemporary preventive healthcare model. To take care of one's health is a mitzvah (a positive commandment and a worthy deed), as is stated in Deuteronomy 4:9: "Take heed of thyself and take care of your lives," and in Deuteronomy 4:15: "Be extremely protective of your lives." The Bible regards life as the highest good, and we are obligated to protect it. If it could help save a life, one *must* (not *may*) violate the Sabbath, eat forbidden foods, or even eat on Yom Kippur—a 24-hour fast and the holiest day of the year.

We have the ability to lead a lifestyle that is compatible with good health. We know from research data that approximately 70% of the factors that determine whether we will get ill are within our control. Science and medicine now have a clear understanding of the causes of many chronic diseases, several of which are called chronic diseases of *lifestyle*. Although your doctor has a duty to advise and direct you in the implementation of preventive care, our health is essentially our own responsibility.

Small lifestyle adjustments can have dramatic effects on our health. Optimizing our nutrition with the best food choices; maintaining a consistent exercise program; giving up smoking; moderating our alcohol intake; protecting ourselves from excessive sun damage; and effectively managing our stress will go a long way to averting the development of disease, will help us age well, and will help us retard deterioration.

Our mental well-being and emotional health also require close attention, as they, too, are vital aspects of our health and quality of life. How remarkable that the Bible stated this thousands of years ago.

The Bible and Talmud: Repository of Medical Wisdom

The Bible is not a book about medicine. The Bible is a book about how to achieve both a physical and spiritual healthy life and journey. And yet so many of the concepts are more relevant than ever. The Bible's message is as "up to date" as its principles of medicine.

The historic approach espoused by Judaism is fundamentally different from that of medicine up until recent times. Only in the recent past has prevention become central in mainstream medicine. While treating sick people is certainly a Torah obligation, Judaism puts a priority on the prevention of disease.

The Bible finds its complement in the Talmud's teachings. The main contribution of Talmudic medicine, like that of biblical medicine, consists not so much of the enumeration of therapeutic methods as it does in expounding upon measures of preventive medicine. Talmudic literature says, "Physical cleanliness is conducive to spiritual purity."

Preventive Medicine in the Bible

The Bible as a guide to preventive medicine is unique because of its many regulations for social hygiene. Of Judaism's 613 commandments, 213 are of a medical nature. Hygiene and prophylaxis became religious mandates designed for the preservation and well-being of the nation. The adage of "an ounce of prevention is worth a pound of cure" finds its origin in the Bible. For example, in order to keep military camps clean, latrines were established outside their bounds, and soldiers were equipped with spades with which they were to dig holes and cover their excrement (Deuteronomy 23: 13-15). Similarly, those who might spread serious diseases were excluded from the camp for specific quarantine periods (Leviticus 15:1-15; Numbers 5:1-4). These same practices are utilized in almost every army in the world today. The ease of the spread of disease caused by mass transportation on planes, trains, and large ships is ever-present. The simple washing of hands is the number one way that life was extended throughout the millennium.

Jewish Dietary Laws: A Jewish Approach to Healthcare

The historic approach espoused by Judaism is fundamentally different from that of medicine up until recent times. As we mentioned earlier, only in the recent past has prevention become central in mainstream medicine. While treating sick people is certainly a Torah obligation, Judaism puts a huge priority on the prevention of disease. The foundation for the Bible's emphasis on preventive medicine can be found by considering the verse in the Torah where God is described as the "Rofeh'—healer" (Exodus 15:26). Rashi (Rabbi Shlomo Yitzhaki, medieval French rabbi and author of the most comprehensive Commentary on both the written and the oral Bible) commented: "I am the Lord Who saves you from these diseases—like a physician who says to a man: 'Do not eat this thing lest it will bring you into danger from this illness.'"

Although keeping kosher implied a higher level of "cleanliness," its more accurate meaning is "proper." The biblical commentaries emphasize that the reason for keeping kosher is not because of cleanliness, although science has demonstrated that it is certainly an unexpected bonus. In biblical Israel, her neighbors consumed pork, and uncooked or undercooked pork is a known cause of trichinosis, a disease marked by abdominal pain and other debilitating symptoms. After the Exodus from Egypt, ancient Jews were forbidden to eat shellfish which may cause allergy or in rare cases cause effects such as anaphylaxis or paralysis.

The following anecdote about Maimonides is instructive. During the period when Maimonides served as the royal physician to the sultan of Egypt, the sultan never became ill. One day the Sultan asked Maimonides, "How do I know that you are an expert physician, inasmuch as during the period that you have been here, I have never been ill, and you have not had the opportunity to test your skills?" Maimonides replied, "In truth, the great and faithful physician is the Holy One, Blessed be He, as it is written: 'I am the Lord, your healer.' And this Great Lord was able to promise His people that because He is their Physician, He will be able to protect them from all the illnesses that were put on Egypt." Maimonides added, "Therefore, we learn that the ability of a physician to prevent illness is a greater proof of his skill, than his ability to cure someone who is already ill" (*Yalkut Lekach Tov*, Shemot, *Beshalach*).

Food Hygiene

Distinctions are made between kosher and non-kosher animals as well. Among the animals, those that have cloven hooves, and chew the cud, may be eaten (Leviticus 11:3). Interestingly, the pig has a split hoof, but it does not chew its cud. The consumption of pork, therefore, is forbidden to Jews. Adherence to this law may provide protection from tapeworm and roundworm infestation.

With regard to fish, there are other rules of kashrut. "These you may eat of all that are in the water: whatever in the water has fins and scales, whether in the seas or in the rivers that you may eat. But all in the seas or in the rivers, those that do not have fins and scales . . . they are an abomination to you" (Leviticus 11:9-10). Sharks and swordfish, which do not have the required fins and scales, are therefore not kosher; they also have high concentrations of mercury, a poisonous element. Shellfish, which are also prohibited, may contain high rates of copper, which might be partly responsible for higher rates of Alzheimer's disease.

The prevention of the spread of infection in modern, "hi-tech" hospitals is a "must" today. To that end, four essential principles remain the building blocks for success:

—isolation of infectious disease

—sterility, cleansing, and the prevention of the spread of infection

—food hygiene

—sanitation

Health Rules of the Bible and Talmud

Health rules of the Bible and Talmud were applicable to city planning, personal hygiene, and social relationships. Even in biblical times, Jews knew that the prevention of disease depended on the isolation and disinfection of clothing and objects by washing

(Talmud Baba Kama 60b); flies were to be avoided as carriers of diseases (Talmud Ketubot 77a); and clean air and sunlight were considered the best cure for diseases (Talmud Ketubot 110b).

The use of toilet paper as an aid to personal hygiene did not come into existence until the 1300s, some 3,400 years later, when the first toilet paper was ordered by the Chinese emperor of the time. Prior to that, everything from grass and leaves to clay (by the Romans) was used as a form of toilet paper. But it is clear that the ancient Hebrews understood the importance of hygiene, as indicated by the rituals of required hand-washing before meals and bathing after the menstrual cycle.

While there do not seem to have been hospitals at the time, there were synagogue halls where the sick could stay. Moreover, there were houses set apart for this purpose, just as in the days of the Bible (II Kings 15). There were also "operating" rooms (*batei shaish*) with marble-paneled walls. Researcher and author Dr. Fred Rosner points out that the Temple had separate rooms in which priests could be examined to determine if they were healthy enough to perform sacred functions.

The seriousness that biblical scholars attached to the importance of proper individual hygiene for the preservation of health is illustrated by the following anecdote from the life of Hillel the holy sage in 100 B.C.

Once when Hillel was about to take leave of his disciples, they said to him: "Master, where are you going?"

He replied: "To do a pious deed."

They asked: "What may that be?"

He replied: "To take a bath."

They asked: "Is that a pious deed?"

He replied: "Yes. If in the theaters and circuses, the images of the king must be kept clean by the man to whom they have been entrusted, how much more is it a duty of man to care for the body, inasmuch as man has been created in the divine image and likeness."

—*Leviticus Rabbah* 34:3

The Bible and Public Health

The validity of the Bible has been firmly authenticated by numerous archaeological discoveries, and thus it remains one of the most circulated and well-known books in history. It is imperative to understand that the health-related laws given in the Bible were to be followed only for ritualistic and spiritual reasons, and not for their inherent advantages in preventing infections and diseases. However, a close study of these many rules and protocols reveals that strict adherence and compliance would have a direct positive effect on public health and community wellness. The high priest, assuming a role analogous to the modern public health officer, would be responsible for ensuring the isolation of individuals carrying infectious diseases. An infected person was denied admittance into the healthy community until the cessation of his disease could be confirmed by physical ascertainment. This practice represents the origin of quarantine, as we know it today. A seemingly remarkable understanding of the germ theory is depicted in laws that require a cleansing "ritual bath" after contact with dead animals or humans. Furthermore, the washing of hands prior to eating undoubtedly reduced the level of germs that could cause gastrointestinal infections.

The Bible apparently recognized that germs could be transmitted, more than 3,000 years before Louis Pasteur discovered that germs actually came from a source and weren't spontaneously generated, as was commonly believed. The Bible states that if an animal dies on something, that article is now considered to be unclean (Leviticus 11:32). Whether or not a transferable infectious agent was being illustrated in the Torah is entirely speculative. However, the people did act on this principle of transferability by implementing strict quarantine protocols. For example, a highly contagious ulcerating skin disease, known as *tzara'at* or *shechin*, is frequently mentioned in the Bible; anyone who came in contact with this infection was to be kept apart from the community in isolation, as noted in Leviticus 13:46: "As long as he has the infection he remains unclean. He must live alone; he must live outside the camp." Once the person has recovered from the disease, the law requires that the person be cleansed by washing all his clothes, shaving off all his hair, and bathing in water. Only after the high priest inspected his sores, and he was declared healed, was he allowed to return; even then, he had to remain outside his tent for seven days (Leviticus 14:8). In fact, these laws were so stringent that refusal to purify oneself could result in banishment by the community (Numbers 19:20).

The Origin of the Word *Quarantine*

Although the success of these practices in promoting public health is a difficult outcome to measure, there is a significant example of its effectiveness in 14th century Italy. At that time, the Black Plague was rampant all across Europe. In attempt to control the spread of this voracious disease, the city leaders of Venice decided to adopt the 40-day segregation practices employed by the Jewish ghettos at the time. After having a profound effect in reducing the disease rates, the practice of segregating infected individuals was beginning to gain acceptance. Hence, the term "quarantine" (*quaranta*, meaning 40) was adopted to refer to the number of days to be spent in isolation.

Other rules, given in Leviticus, address the safety of the food and water supply, recognizing that contact with "unclean" items made a clean item also "unclean." The disposal of animal waste and human sewage, especially important during times of war, is also described, often with astounding explicitness. Because many of these religious laws required one to become physically clean, it is evident that a community-level pursuit of spiritual purity would result in high dividends for public health. Anything that an unclean person touched would become unclean, and anyone who touched it became unclean (Numbers 19:22).

Hygiene and Infection Control

In biblical times, the spectrum of therapeutics available to the Hebrews was extremely limited. Although there is a brief mention of physicians and surgical procedures in the Talmud, biblical medicine places a strong emphasis on prevention through hygiene and infection control. The importance of prevention in the role of biblical health is in accord with the belief at the time regarding the etiology of disease. Disinfection was a well-known practice that was commonly employed in ancient Israel. Items that could withstand heat were purified in fire, while those that could not be purified in that manner were washed in water (Numbers 31:22-23).

It was also recognized that the use of different materials was related to varying degrees of risk for disease. For cooking instruments, the law clearly states that clay pots were to be broken after they were used for cooking. Being made of porous materials, clay pots are an excellent source of microorganisms that live off the food in the pores. However, if a bronze pot is used for cooking, it must be "scoured and rinsed with water" (Leviticus 6:28) before it can be used again. Again the dietary laws (of kashrut) made sense when examining the ritual customs as medical procedure.

The law recognized that animals were a major reservoir for infectious agents. "The fat of an animal found dead or torn by wild animals may be used for any other purpose, but you must note eat it" (Leviticus 7:24). Animal waste disposal was not a problem either. The Jews were instructed not only to take the carcass outside the camp, but also to then burn it in a wood fire (Leviticus 4:11-12). This would obviously prevent wild animals from being attracted to the carcass and would avoid the spread of infection to other animals.

Human waste was also dealt with effectively during times of war. Soldiers were instructed to designate a specific place where they could relieve themselves. In addition, they were given clear instructions to carry something to dig with, in order to "dig a hole and cover up your excrement" (Deuteronomy 23:13).

Hand Washing: Way Before Medical Science

According to the Bible, it was common practice to wash one's hands before eating, holding to the tradition of the elders. Hand washing is one of the most difficult tasks for today's healthcare workers to remember, and yet it is one of the easiest to do. These simple practices can have a profound impact on the health of an individual, the health of an isolated community, such as a hospital, and even the health of the community at large. Until the late 1800s, hand washing was believed to be of no value in preventing disease and was looked upon as a complete waste of time. The value of hand washing was first brought to light when the Hungarian physician Ignaz Semmelweis, who happened to be Jewish, noticed that mothers whose babies were delivered by medical students had a 15 to 30 percent higher rate of puerperal fever than those whose babies were delivered by midwives. Realizing that the medical students spent time studying cadavers before delivering babies, he implemented a policy of hand washing in chlorinated lime that immediately yielded a drastic reduction in the incidence of the disease. Despite all the evidence, Semmelweis continued to be ridiculed by the medical community, and his practices were never adopted during his lifetime.

Many other scientists were proven right after being ostracized by fellow professional peers, including Dr. Barry Marshall and fellow Australian Dr. Robin Warren, who discovered that *H-pylori or—Helicobacter pylori* (bacteria in the digestive tract)—was the main cause of peptic ulcers (not stress, as previously thought). Ultimately, they were proven correct and awarded the Nobel Prize for Medicine in 2005.

Healing from Minerals and Sea Salt

When talking about inflammation and preventive medicine, it is important to note the words of Genesis 14:3: "All these were joined together in the vale of Siddim, which is the salt sea." This passage refers to a war conducted by four kings against five at the Dead Sea. Since the time of Cleopatra, people from all walks of life have come to the Dead Sea near Masada and Ein Gedi to bathe at the lowest point on Earth, 1,300 feet below sea level. Evidence has shown that people with aliments from psoriasis to arthritis have had relief to varying degrees due to the high concentration of salt (sodium, which is a natural anti-inflammatory), along with a high concentration of minerals such as magnesium and bromine. People from all over the world—especially from Germany and Russia—visit the Dead Sea today. Even King David spent time in hiding from Saul near the Dead Sea: "And David went up from thence, and dwelt in strongholds at Ein Gedi" (I Samuel 23:29).

Ritual Baths

In biblical times, visiting the Tabernacle was one of the most sacred events. In order to even come into the Temple courtyard, people had to be spiritually pure. For this purpose, one would partake in a ceremonial cleansing in a ritual bath. Other indications for taking a ritual bath included after having touched a dead animal or body; after having entered the house of a deceased person; for a man, after having had a seminal emission, or for a woman after menses; and especially after recovery from an infectious disease (Numbers 19:19-22).

So important was the ritual bath that one was constructed next to every synagogue. The individual, in preparing to take the ritual bath, had to remove all rings and jewelry; nothing was to come between the individual and the water.

The quality of the water was also very important. The Bible is very clear that the water to be used had to be fresh water, such as that from a stream or from collected rain (Leviticus 15:13). The individual has to wash his/her clothes and bathe in the water before he/she will be clean. Once the person has bathed, the water, now considered unclean, will not be used again.

Clearly, this is a spiritually purifying ritual, but all the accompanying details ensure physical cleansing too.

Circumcision

Circumcision is mentioned in Genesis, with respect to Abraham and Isaac, who lived almost 2,000 years ago.

For some time there have been questions as to any possible preventive health benefits from circumcision, which is a central aspect of Jewish life and law.

In Genesis 17:9-13, God said to Abraham, "As for you, you must keep My covenant, you and your descendants after you for the generations to come. This is My covenant with you and your descendants after you, the covenant you are to keep: Every male among you shall be circumcised. You are to undergo circumcision, and it will be the sign of the covenant between Me and you. For generations to come, every male among you who is eight days old must be circumcised. My covenant in your flesh is to be an everlasting covenant."

Let's look at the medical realities of the advantages of circumcision. Tangentially, the reason why the *brit milah*, circumcision, occurs on the eighth day of a newborn's life is that both vitamin K and prothrombin is at its peak on the eighth day, which allows for clotting. This vitamin received the letter K, because the initial discoveries were reported in a German journal, in which it was designated as a "koagulation" vitamin.

The evidence is overwhelming that circumcision before the age of one decreases the rate of penile cancer among men and reduces the risk of cervical cancer and HPV (human papilloma virus) in female partners. A 2002 study in Denmark showed a fivefold lower rate of penile cancer in men who were circumcised. Another multinational study that same year, initiated and conducted by the International Agency of Research on Cancer and published in the *New England Journal of Medicine*, showed that a woman was 5.6 times more likely to contract cervical cancer if her partner was uncircumcised. Cervical HPV infection was associated with a 77-fold increase in cervical cancer. Parents should take note: Women, including teenage girls, should be vaccinated with the HPV vaccine (with a doctor's knowledge). The vaccine acts against HPV 16 and HPV 18, which are associated with 70 percent of the cases of HPV-related cervical cancer.

There is new evidence that HPV is directly associated with oral cancers in both men and women. In the case of men, tonsil cancer has increased almost threefold since the 1970s, and the increased incidence of head and neck cancers is also directly linked to contracting HPV orally. So the same vaccines for teenage girls should be given to teenage boys as well (again with a doctor's knowledge and concurrence).

Public Health References throughout the Bible

There are numerous references throughout the Bible on various public health and preventive medical concerns such as sterility, cleansing, and the prevention of the spread of infection (Leviticus 15:211); abnormal bodily discharge—for example, infectious diarrhea (Leviticus 12:2); infectious disease, which was the most common cause of death in biblical times (Numbers 19:11); and the safe disposal of waste as instructed in Deuteronomy 23:1213 (and previously cited in our section on Hygiene and Infection Control): "Designate a place outside the camp where you can go to relieve yourself. As part of your equipment, have something to dig with, and when you relieve yourself, dig a hole and cover up your excrement."

Maimonides and Preventive Health

Maimonides, royal physician to the sultan of Egypt, Rabbi, astronomer and codifier of Jewish law espoused much of the Bible's guidelines to preventive health in his work entitled "*Hanhagat Habriut*—or Pathway of Health." He emphasized optimal nutrition abounding in natural foods, not overeating but eating until satiated, movement as the fundamental of good health and emotional well-being. All of these recommendations predate the modern preventive health movement and hundreds of diet programs by almost three thousand years.

Overall health is not just nourishment of the body, but of the soul as well. "My son, do not forget my teaching, but keep my commands in your heart, for they will prolong your life many years and bring you prosperity . . . This will bring health to your body and nourishment to your bones" (Proverbs 3:1-2, 8).

Chapter 7

Work and Stress

Work: Meaningful Fulfillment or Curse?

Some people associate work with creativity, productivity, positive challenges, significance, pride of accomplishment, enjoyable relationships, and stimulating challenges. Others associate it with dreary toil, futility, injustice, and joyless malaise. The Bible provides mixed signals concerning the nature and value of work. From one perspective, God's word speaks of work as a vehicle of expression and a means of provision that can impart satisfaction and a sense of accomplishment. However after the fall, work was mandated as a punishment or at least as a consequence. "Thou will eat bread, by the sweat of thy brow." Notwithstanding this, meaningful endeavor seems to be the overriding message from the Bible. Even prior to the fall, God mandated the fulfillment that is to be found in labor: "The Lord God took the man and put him in the Garden of Eden to work it and take care of it" (Genesis 2:15).

Stressed-Out: A Universal Malady

Richard Swenson, physician, researcher, and author describes in his book *Margin,* that the society in which we live is really troubled. He says, "We are careening along at breakneck speed." Most of our major troubles are due to the incredible stress burden with which we live. The work pressures, demands, expectations, and deadlines keep us in a continual state of adrenalin secretion.

Add to this, the digital age of constantly remaining plugged in and switched on. Financial pressures, family responsibilities, and the struggles of life plague us as we hurtle through our lives at a constantly hurrying pace. This can often make us sick.

Not all Stress is Bad

Notwithstanding all of the above, the reality is that not all stress is bad. *Eustress*, the term for "good stress" can better be described as ambition, drive, motivation, passion, or challenge. The challenge of work, goals, and vision keep one motivated and focused. Unfortunately, the positive stress is usually stretched beyond a point and most of us live with overwhelming, damaging, negative stress.

Is Stress a Mental State?

Most people seem to think of stress as a mental or emotional condition such as feeling overwhelmed, overloaded, or burdened with too much work. The reality is that stress is a physical state too, caused by the effects of adrenalin on the body.

Acute stress is simply defined as the release of adrenalin in response to a danger or challenge. The body is designed to revert to a relaxed state after the danger or threat is removed. Unfortunately most of the time the stress becomes unrelenting, creating a state of chronic adrenalin overload. Stress is one of the most significant triggers of heart disease, acute and chronic illness, burnout and depression, and is a powerful factor in weakening immunity.

The Stress Response

The Stress Response is a remarkable physiological function. It is a primitive survival mechanism designed to protect the body from harm. It enables us to get out of danger quickly.

With the outpouring of adrenalin the body is primed for action. Heart rate and blood pressure are increased to enable blood to reach the muscles and the peripheries of the body. In order to either fight or flee the danger, muscles become tense, breathing becomes shallow, and the body is in a heightened state of alertness.

With relaxation, the exact opposite occurs: breathing deepens; pulse and blood pressure decrease; and muscles relax. During this parasympathetic or relaxation phase, blood is diverted back to essential organ function and cellular repair and regeneration takes place.

The Stress response is an amazing system for escaping burning buildings or fighting intruders. The problem is that the pressure and pace of work and life continually send "danger" messages to the body. All the while we are sitting behind a desk, responding to emails, managing deadlines, or presenting at meetings. We are not in danger, but our body is firing away on a non- stop adrenalin rush. This maintains our blood pressure at a constantly high level, the pulse at a racing speed, and shallow breathing unable to oxygenate all body organs. The blood is diverted away from essential functioning.

Most of the time when adrenalin is released there is no "fight or fleeing", but the body and muscles are primed for action. This may result in headaches, irritable colon, neck spasm, hypertension, and possible immune depression.

Chronic Adaptation to Stress

The problem is that this stress cycle does not end there. If there is no respite from the interminable release of adrenalin (due to persistent demands and stress triggers), there is a secondary phase of the stress response. This response is called the Adaptation Phase; the body adapts to the chronic stress.

When this occurs, the brain will trigger the release of yet another hormone to assist adrenalin. This stress hormone is called *cortisol*; it acts as a powerful painkiller that will dampen any discomfort. (Hence you will often hear from chronically stressed individuals, *"But I don't even feel stressed!"*) Cortisol is an extremely effective anti-inflammatory agent, but unfortunately, it also corrodes muscles, bones, and immunity.

The Daily Grind

The body response to an acute stress is almost identical whether we are facing a sudden danger or the unexpected news of retrenchment. However, most of our stress is not from these sudden dangers or traumas but rather the relentless pursuit of the daily grind. Work commitments, long hours, high demands and expectations, and the unrelenting fast pace create an adrenalin state that is perpetually switched-on.

The irony is that the very body mechanism designed to protect us from harm, may cause an enormous amount of body damage if it continues unabated.

A Divinely Ordained Antidote for Stress

There is a worldwide search for the finest stress management techniques. Good quality sleep, optimal nutrition, and adequate exercise are essential. Undoubtedly, strategies such as mindfulness and meditation are invaluable, and are finally breaking through into mainstream health practices. But we can find a remarkable remedy within the Bible.

God understood the importance of rest for the body and soul by commanding us to observe a day for recharging our energies. This concept was set forth repeatedly in the Old Testament. Exodus 20:8-11 reads: "Remember the Sabbath day to keep it holy. Six days you shall labor and do all your work, but the seventh day is a Sabbath to the Lord your God. On it, you shall not do any work, neither you, nor your son or daughter, nor your manservant or maidservant, nor your animals, nor the alien within your gates. For in six days the Lord made the heavens and the earth, the sea, and all that is in them, but He rested on the seventh day. Therefore, the Lord blessed the Sabbath day and made it holy." This instruction, which comprises the Fourth Commandment, is repeated almost word for word in Deuteronomy 5:12–15.

Why the emphasis?

If twice isn't enough to bring the message home, He mentions it a third time in Exodus 31:12-32 when the Lord said to Moses,

"Say to the Israelites, 'You must observe my Sabbath. This will be a sign between Me and you for the generations to come, so you may know that I am the Lord, Who makes you holy. Observe the Sabbath, because it is holy to you. For six days, work is to be done, but the seventh day is a Sabbath of rest, holy to the Lord. The Israelites are to observe the Sabbath, celebrating it for generations to come as a lasting covenant. It will be a sign between me and the Israelites forever, for in six days the Lord made the heavens and the earth and on the seventh day he abstained from work and rested.'"

We, too, have to learn to recharge our batteries again; so perhaps the greatest gift God gave to the world is the concept of a Sabbath, however we intend to observe that day. Perhaps one of the greatest gifts the Hebrews shared with the world is "TGIF."

The Science of Rest

What a concept—rest! Rest is such a basic prerequisite for health and performance, yet most of us are chronically sleep-deprived and exhausted much of the time. Numerous studies in the past few years, including some of the most important from the Mayo Clinic, Harvard, and the University of Pennsylvania, demonstrate that insufficient sleep—generally less than six hours of sleep a night—can affect one's immune system, lead to decline in cognitive function, higher blood pressure, cardiovascular complications, depression, and even a greater incidence of obesity and stroke. In 1850, the average person slept nine and one-half hours per night. Now, thanks to electricity, late-night TV, Internet, smartphones, and 24/7 connectivity, the figure is far less than seven hours per night and declining. We are undoubtedly the most frazzled and sleep-deprived generation ever.

A Call to Rest

Work is not only a blessing from God; it is also a command. The first half of the Fourth Commandment says: "Six days you shall labor and do all your work" (Exodus 20:9). However, the second half of that commandment is a call to rest: "But the seventh day is a Sabbath to the Lord your God. On it you shall not do any work . . ." (Exodus 20:10). Rest is just as much a part of the Creation ordinance as work. The evidence is overwhelming that rest and sleep are important to support our immune system, to fend off disease, to maintain memory, and to keep our metabolism in check.

A Badge of Honor

We carry stress around like a badge of honor. This is especially true among business and community leaders where the lie is propagated that to be overbooked is to be important.

In his book *Shoulder to Shoulder,* Dr. Rodney L. Cooper defines stress as "the response of a sympathetic nervous system to a perceived or actual threat." He adds that stress is basically the way our body responds to perceived or actual danger. Our blood pressure rises, and our muscle strength increases. We are ready to fight or to flee (as discussed earlier). Stress isn't the cause of this response, but the effect. In essence, stress is a reaction to danger—real or imagined.

An Example from the Bible: Saul and David

Dr. Cooper's definition of stress certainly describes what happened to King Saul after David had killed Goliath:

> When the men were returning home after David had killed the Philistine, the women came out from all the towns of Israel to meet King Saul with singing and dancing, with joyful songs, and with tambourines and lutes. As they danced, they sang: "Saul has slain his thousands, and David his tens of thousands."
>
> Saul was very angry; this refrain galled him. "They have credited David with tens of thousands," he thought, "but me with only thousands. What more can he get but the

kingdom?" And from that time on Saul kept a jealous eye on David.

The next day an evil spirit from God came forcefully upon Saul. He was prophesying in his house, while David was playing the harp, as he usually did. Saul had a spear in his hand and he hurled it, saying to himself, "I'll pin David to the wall." But David eluded him twice.

—I Samuel 18:6-11

Sensing that David was a threat to his position, the king's blood pressure skyrocketed, his heart rate increased, and his muscles tightened. Overcome with rage, he hurled a spear at David, who narrowly escaped. In that instance, Saul's response was to a perceived rather than an actual danger. David had no intention of overthrowing the king, nor would he have used his newfound popularity to ease Saul out of power. Saul naturally assumed that David was like himself. Unfortunately, one of Saul's shortcomings as a leader was his inability to deal constructively with his perceptions of danger. That weakness undermined his mental health as well as the stability of his throne.

Building Resilience

In the "University of Life," stress and affliction are not elective courses; they're a required part of the curriculum. Stress, as we now know is not necessarily a negative feature. It enhances personal development and growth.

As we mentioned earllier, most of the stress we experience is good for us. The primary issue is how we respond to that pressure. Although external circumstances may cause the stress, it is always our internal responses to those external forces that create the damage. We have so little, if any, control over our personal situations. The only thing we can consistently control is our response. Resilient individuals view stressful situations as an opportunity for growth.

With weight and strength training, we build ourselves up by intentionally inducing stress on our muscles. Why does the correlation between the physical and the spiritual so often elude us? We much prefer to go to a physical gym but abide in a spiritual lounge. We need to grow our spiritual muscle too and build resilience on all levels.

The Illusion of Control

Much of the stress in our lives comes about because of our insistence on maintaining the illusion of control. We so desperately want to be strong enough to handle the trials and tribulations of life that we literally drive ourselves into the ground rather than expose vulnerability or admit our desperate need for some assistance.

Only in those moments of rare clarity that come from bottoming-out, will we allow ourselves to admit how little control we actually have. In those moments, the only thing we can possibly do is choose to throw ourselves headlong into the grace of God. In these moments, the pain and suffering may actually drive us to Him.

Let's look to the biblical text for some insight. When we think of stress, how many of us could have handled what Job went through, losing his children, all his wealth, and everything he had? Each day we read and hear of the horrors and misery that markedly overshadow our own personal stress. When we look at the poverty, war, crime, and terrorism around the globe, we wonder how it is possible for us to be stressed by some of the mundane events of our daily lives. But the fact is that *stress is personal* and a real occurrence for each of us, albeit experienced in so many different ways.

Even God Himself, in Whose image we are created, was stressed by mankind, as expressed in Genesis 6:5-8: "Then the Lord saw that the wickedness of man was great in the earth, and that every intent of the thoughts of his heart was only evil continually. And the Lord was sorry that He had made man on the earth, and He was grieved in His heart. So the Lord said, 'I will destroy man whom I have created from the face of the earth, man and beast, creeping thing and birds of the air, for I am sorry that I have made them.' But Noah found grace in the eyes of the Lord." God understood that one individual, Noah, could turn the tide.

Leadership and Stress: A Lesson from King David

Leaders under the immense pressure of identifying and solving problems can quickly reach high levels of stress. Fortunately, King David offers some insight intended to help leaders manage their stress in Psalms 23:1-6: "The Lord is my shepherd, I shall not want. He makes me lie down in green pastures, He leads me beside still waters, He restores my soul. He guides me in paths of righteousness for His name's sake. Even though I walk through the valley of the shadow of death, I will fear no evil, for You are with me; your rod and your staff, they comfort me. You prepare a table before me in the presence of my enemies. You anoint my head with oil; my cup overflows. Surely goodness and mercy will follow me all the days of my life, and I will dwell in the house of the Lord forever."

In this psalm, King David—who often faced overwhelming pressure—told his readers where he found his solace and security. This psalm can afford comfort to anyone, at anytime; but we all find it especially relevant when we are under stress.

Or we can turn to Psalm 27: 1, 3: "The Lord is my light and my salvation; whom shall I fear? The Lord is the stronghold of my life; of whom shall I be afraid? Though an army encamps against me, my heart shall not fear; though war rise up against me, yet I will be confident." Today this can possibly be applied to everyday battles with traffic, the economy, pollution, expenses, and life's small everyday battles.

Ask for Help and Advice: A Lesson from Moses

Even Moses found it hard to handle all the stress, and he finally asked his father-in-law, Jethro, for advice in Exodus 18:1-27: "And so it was, on the next day, that Moses sat to judge the people;

and the people stood before Moses from morning until evening." Then, when Moses' father-in-law saw all that he did for the people, he asked, "What is this thing that you are doing for the people? Why do you alone sit, and all the people stand before you from morning until evening?" And Moses replied, "Because the people come to me to inquire of God. When they have a difficulty, they come to me, and I judge between one and another; and I make known the statutes of God and His laws."

In other words, it is okay to delegate. What better advice could there be for leaders?

Stress and Work

Sixty percent of lost workdays each year can be attributed to stress. In addition, an estimated 75 to 90 percent of visits to health-care providers are prompted by stress-related conditions, costing employers in increased healthcare costs.

Stress also can have a direct effect on the way people handle their jobs. Employees under stress may become disorganized, angry, depressed, have trouble concentrating, make more mistakes, or just stop caring about their work.

The *Wall Street Journal* reported that one-third of people surveyed considered quitting their jobs because of stress; 14 percent actually did. According to a *Happiness at Work* survey (NicMarks New Economics Foundation, London 2012), happy workers are 31% higher in productivity, have 37% higher sales, and demonstrate an increase in creativity that is three times the expected level.

Pay on Time!

We have a direct impact on our employees' health and well-being and on that of their families. The atmosphere and culture in the work environment has a direct impact on stress. Whether he or she is feeling respect, fear, intimidation, or embarrassment, the employee will inevitably bring home the stress of those emotions, which will affect his spouse and children.

What possible link exists between employers, employees, stress, and the Bible? On more than one occasion, the Bible stresses the importance of this topic. The Bible specifies that one must pay one's worker on the day that he completes his work. Leviticus 19:13 reads: "You shall not leave (with you) the payment of a worker overnight until the morning." Deuteronomy 24:15 says: "On his day you should give his wages, the sun should not set on it, because he is a poor man and his life depends on it . . ." The Bible understood the significance that often a worker is in urgent need of his wages—for buying food or to provide other needs—and that to postpone paying him may cause undue distress.

Work: Boredom or Satisfaction? Ecclesiastes

It is perfectly okay for work to be repetitive. Regardless of the type of work one is engaged in, much of the time there are demands and expectations, and sometimes work may become monotonous. Regardless of the nature of the work, it can become mundane, boring, and frustrating. A bus driver, computer, programmer, office assistant, or even a surgeon may get to the point where the work is repetitive and unsatisfying. But life is not merely about working and resting from our labors. It is also about trying to find a purpose and meaning through it all.

Dr. Viktor Frankl, author, psychiatrist, holocaust survivor, and the father of the school of logotherapy, sheds light on this topic in his most famous work *Man's Search for Meaning* when he wrote that we should strive to find meaning in the mundane, even through suffering, in attempting to contribute to the world around us.

The wisdom is perhaps in stepping back intermittently and viewing the bigger picture, which includes the person's gratification, the contribution to society, or the solving of a problem.

Working itself may create great satisfaction; the key is finding purpose through it all. Fulfillment from work is explicitly spoken of in the Bible. Ecclesiastes 3:13 tells us: "That everyone may eat and drink, and find satisfaction in all his toil—this is the gift of God."

Ecclesiastes offers a middle position that acknowledges both the joys and the heartaches of work. The Teacher cautions us to avoid both extremes—that of taking work too seriously and regarding it as a totally futile endeavor. So from one perspective, "A man can do nothing better than to eat and drink and find satisfaction in his work" (v. 24). But from another vantage point, the same Teacher laments that "work . . . is meaningless, a chasing after the wind" (v. 17). Putting these pieces together, we can observe that one key to stress management is a realistic satisfaction in work, while avoiding the pitfall of turning it into an idol. We should hold onto our work with a loose grip, because our true source of significance and security is in our family and our belief system, not solely from our occupation. We also learn that the sole pursuit of biblical or Godly studies is not the ultimate pursuit. A balance between both work and studies is necessary.

In fact, in *Ethics of the Fathers* 2:2, we find: "Torah learning is best combined with an occupation, because the effort of both will keep one from sin."

Work as a Commandment; Work as a Blessing

So what does the Bible say about working? From Psalms 128:2: "You shall eat the fruit of the labor of your hands; you shall be blessed, and it shall be well with you." Thus, work is not just a blessing from God, but also a commandment.

Rarely does God give us a reason for His commands. But he does for the Fourth Commandment. As we previously noted, He says that we are to take a day off from our work because God himself did the same in Exodus 20:11: "For in six days the Lord made the heavens and the earth, the sea, and all that is in them, but He rested on the seventh day. Therefore the Lord blessed the Sabbath day and made it holy."

A Rhythm of Work and Rest

Undoubtedly, God could have accomplished all His work at once. It would not have taxed God to cram all six days' worth of

Creation into one day. But the Almighty was establishing a pattern for us to follow—a rhythm of work and rest. God worked, and then He rested.

We get overwhelmed. We get anxious. We get depressed. We collapse. We burn out. There is such scientific clarity regarding the inability of a human to function at high intensity for long periods of time. All of the universe, creation, and nature—as well as the human body—are pulse-like, oscillating between contraction and expansion. Nothing can remain in an expanded state for long periods. It simply snaps, breaks, or collapses.

The Causes of Chronic Stress

On the hierarchy of stress, there is no doubt that death of a loved one is by the far the most extreme. This is followed by divorce, birth of a baby (albeit joyous), and migration and relocation, including simply moving into a new house.

A recent study conducted by the American Psychological Association revealed that 73 percent of people surveyed cited money problems as a significant source of stress. After death, divorce, and childhood trauma, financial issues even surpass health-related issues when it comes to triggering significant stress.

Stress: A Threat to Health in Biblical Times and Now

Researchers have documented that increased stress levels can lead to changes in psychological and physiological functioning. In addition to changes in the usual stress hormones, such as adrenalin and cortisol, many other chemical messengers are influenced by exposure to stressors. Production and release of prolactin, growth hormone, insulin, and thyroid hormones can be affected by physical and emotional stress. Levels of nerve proteins (called neurotransmitters) and various cells in the immune system can also be affected by stress.

As far back as biblical times stress has been an enormous health issue. The biblical stressors were far more acute than ours and on a grander scale. Way back 3,500 years ago, the major stressors involved simple aspects of life—many of which are things we take for granted today—like finding food, shelter, protection from wild animals, and the constant threat of war from neighboring tribes. (The Israelites fought such enemies as the Midanites, Edomites, Amorites, and the Amalekites.) Notwithstanding these examples, the insidious chronic stress of our times—albeit less dramatic than warding off marauders or wild beasts—also has a sinister effect on our health.

Depression and Suicide

With more than 150 million sufferers globally, millions of whom require antidepressant medication, depression is now a worldwide epidemic. Although stress is a contributing factor and a trigger for suicide, depression, anxiety, and mental illness are extremely common and often totally unrelated to stress. They should be fully investigated and treated with a combination of therapies, including psychotherapy and medication.

Suicide in young people has become the number one cause of death in the United States (and in many other countries), surpassing car accidents with more than 35,000 suicides in 2012. Even more alarming is that in 2000, 13 percent of American teenagers between 14 and 17 years of age contemplated suicide, and a third of them actually tried it, according to the Substance Abuse and Mental Health Service Administration (SAMHSA). In addition, 1.4 million teenagers were exposed to a major depressive episode in the last year, and female teenagers are three times more likely than boys to experience such depression.

There are accounts of biblical figures who have committed suicide, such as King Saul (I Samuel 31:45) and Samson (Judges 16:30). Also, the 96 martyrs of Masada and countless others during the Holocaust and Inquisition and other dire episodes of Jewish history committed suicide, either to escape torture or for *Kiddush Hashem*, "sanctification of God." Even Jonah and Elijah plead to die (Jonah 4:4 and I Kings 19:4).

In reality the rabbis who have ordained Jewish law prohibit suicide. Perhaps it is more important for each of us "to love thy neighbor as thyself" and to have compassion for those who are depressed, stressed, and suffering, and to reach out and help. Mental illness requires attention, intervention, and treatment. Do not ignore it and hope it will go away.

Suicide and depression have become international epidemics. According to the WHO (World Health Organization, 2013), many Eastern bloc countries including: Lithuania, Belarus, Estonia, and Hungary had some of the highest rates of suicide and depression per capita: Other countries surveyed included Guyana, Kazakhstan, Greenland, and Finland, Australia, and particularly New Zealand; South Korea and Japan have the dubious distinction of being the "leaders" among worldwide nations.

Stress-Relieving Strategies

There is an antidote to stress and its impact on performance and competence. Not surprisingly, it's rest! It's not how long you take off that matters most, but how skillfully you use these very short periods of renewal. Get up from your desk and stretch your muscles. Take a short walk. The simplest way to recharge energy is by breathing. You can dramatically lower your heart rate, your blood pressure, and your muscle tension in as little as thirty seconds. Learning to practice mindfulness and meditation are very effective ways to defuse stress, strengthen neural connections, oxygenate the brain, and enhance powerful brain neurotransmitters. Although a power nap is near impossible for most office workers, a short nap for 10–15 minutes is an undeniably powerful tool. If you can take a nap anytime between 1 and 4 p.m., it will give you a surge of energy and astonishing productivity for the rest of the afternoon. Although the prevailing work ethic in most companies is that downtime is time wasted, the researched data is compelling. Cognitive function, creativity, and overall performance levels have been shown to improve dramatically after a short power nap. Few employers will sanction naps, but even sitting back in your chair and closing your eyes for a few minutes can be restorative.

Self-Awareness and Loving-Kindness

An important step towards managing stress is to define the problem. Is the stress work related? Is it stress at home or due to problems in relationships? Is it truly stress or could it possibly be depression or anxiety?

Depression and/or anxiety can certainly be precipitated by stress, but may also be totally unrelated to stress. Self-awareness and self-knowledge are vital in addressing our emotional and mental well-being. All of us are exposed to different levels of stress at different times of our lives. The challenge lies in how to individually cope with our stresses and how can we help others to cope with theirs. In Isaiah 25:4, we find: "You have been a refuge for the poor, a refuge for the needy in their distress, a shelter from the storm and a shade from the heat." Even if we are not personally experiencing stress, it is a huge act of loving-kindness to provide a buffer to help heal others' stress.

Exercise

With regular exercise, your body becomes stronger, functions more efficiently, and has greater endurance. Balancing of your hormones, the increase in your serotonin levels, and the release of endorphins all contribute to improving your mood and relieving your stress. But exercise has another powerful effect.

When you are exercising you do not worry! You are actually resting the nerve cells in the brain that worry, giving those cells time to renew themselves. Exercise is the single most effective method to turn off the continuous pumping of adrenalin and to thus allow the body to go into rest mode once the physical activity such as jogging, swimming, cycling, or walking is completed.

Optimal Nutrition

Excellent nutrition can certainly aid the body in building up resilience against the onslaught of stress. In Chapter 3, Nutrition and the Bible, we have provided an extensive review of the healing properties of many foodstuffs.

It is worth noting that some of these foods may help the body build resilience against the physical effects of stress. Fruits and vegetables with high antioxidant contents; low glycemic carbohydrates that provide sustained energy; vitamin-abundant grains; and fish are well worth consuming. Some examples include:

- Blueberries and oranges, with their high vitamin C content, have been shown to give the body added reserves in times of high stress;
- Apricots, one of the few fruits that were readily available in biblical days, are rich in magnesium, which acts to relax muscle tissue;
- Kale, broccoli, and other dark green leafy vegetables may calm nerves because of their high potassium content
- Vitamin B-12 is, one of the important vitamins and may play a role in preventing depression;
- Eggs and fatty fish, including mackerel, herring, salmon, cod, and sardines contain omega 3 fatty acids that are vital for optimal neuronal functioning;
- A supply of serotonin-producing carbohydrates such as whole grains including sweet potatoes, bulgur wheat, quinoa, oats, and brown rice do not spike blood sugar levels and are essential for maintaining a stable mood and high levels of concentration;
- Even a little dark chocolate can go a long way because the cocoa contains monoamine oxidase inhibitors (MAOs) that allow both dopamine and serotonin to maintain higher concentrations in the blood stream and brain.

Overeating, which leads to obesity, was understood in biblical days, as noted in Proverbs 21:23: "One who guards his mouth and tongue saves his soul from affliction." One can interpret both from speaking ill will about someone else as well as protecting one's health from overeating. Also, Rambam stated: "Overeating is like poison to anyone's body. It is the main source of all illness. Most illnesses in which obesity afflicts a person are caused by harmful foods or by filling his belly and overeating, even of healthful foods." He also wrote in *Hilchot Deiot* 4:15: "As long as you exercise, take care not to eat to the point of satiation, and keep your bowels soft, you will not fall ill, and your strength will increase. . . .The opposite is true of someone who leads a sedentary life and takes no exercise."

Music

Music can be a very powerful tool in combatting stress. Samuel I 16:23 states: ". . . and whenever the tormenting spirit from God troubled Saul, David [the future King David] would play the harp. Then Saul would feel better, and the tormenting spirit would go away."

Meditation

The Bible actually commands us to meditate. In Joshua 1:8, God says to meditate on His word day and night so we will obey it. In Psalm 1:2, we read about King David: "His delight is in the law of the Lord and in his law, he meditates day and night." Actually the Bible mentions meditate or meditation 20 times.

Effective stress-relieving methods, such as meditation and breathing exercises provide the body with a physiological experience opposite to stress. They allow the mind and body time to repair, regenerate, and recover from the wear and tear of everyday strain. Research has revealed that taking a power nap or meditating during the day boosts your cellular function and enhances memory. Even the Mayo Clinic website suggests meditation to help people manage symptoms of conditions such as: anxiety disorders, asthma, cancer, depression, heart disease, high blood pressure, pain, and sleep problems.

Chapter 8

Medical Ethics

The Sanctity of Life

Saving and respecting another human being's life is so important that Rabbi Yochanan, a member of the Sanhedrin (the council of sages that existed more than 2,000 years ago) said, "If someone's life is in danger, one should transgress all the laws of the Bible to save this person's life" (Sanhedrin 84a). Perhaps this essence of the Bible has been encapsulated in the concept of *tikun olam,* simply translated as "repairing the world," as it suggests humanity's shared responsibility to heal, repair, and transform the world. In the Judeo Bible the concept of *tikkun olam* originated in the early rabbinic period. The concept was given new meanings in the mystical texts of the Kabbalah of the medieval period, and has come to possess further connotations in modern Judaism, including social action and the pursuit of social justice.

First, Do No Harm

Historically, western medical ethics may be traced to guidelines on the duty of physicians in antiquity, such as the Hippocratic Oath, and to early rabbinic teachings. *Primum non nocere* is a Latin phrase that means "first, do no harm." As one of the precepts of medical ethics that is taught in medical schools throughout the world, it is a fundamental principle of the practice of medicine. As King Solomon said in Psalms 105:15: "Do not touch my anointed

97

ones; do my prophets no harm." Another way to state it is that, given an existing problem, it may be better to do nothing than to risk causing more harm than good. It reminds the physician and other health-care providers that they must consider the possible harm that any intervention might cause. The tenets of the oath are invoked when debating the use of an intervention that carries an obvious risk of harm but a less certain chance of benefit.

In the medieval and early modern period, the topic of *ethics and patients* is indebted to Maimonides, who applied his skills, both as a physician and a great Torah scholar. Later, authors such as the British physician Dr. Thomas Percival (1740-1804) of Manchester wrote about "medical jurisprudence" and reportedly coined the phrase "medical ethics." In 1847, the American Medical Association adopted its first code of ethics, which was based in large part on Percival's work.

This moral code and moral justification is needed to guide the physician in his actions. We learn from Hebrew Scriptures the value of life. In the Book of Genesis, God said, "Let us make man in our image and likeness" (Genesis 1:26); and we learn that God instilled the "breath of life" in man (Genesis 2:7). Because all human beings are created in God's image and given the breath of life, we are called to respect the dignity of each human being.

Doctor-Patient Relationship

As we read in the Book of Exodus, God gave Moses the Ten Commandments. The Sixth Commandment, concerning the sanctity of life, clearly and directly states: "Thou shalt not murder" (Exodus 20:13). The Book of Leviticus, the third book of the Pentateuch, tells the people "to love your neighbor as yourself" (Leviticus 19:18). The Ten Commandments are repeated in the Book of Deuteronomy 5:6-21. The Ten Commandments are also the ethical basis for the doctor-patient relationship. Essential to this relationship is the element of trust. The patient trusts the physician to counsel him to make the right decision regarding his care, to ensure his privacy, and to be his advocate. The physician should be compassionate, truthful, and respectful of the personal dignity of the patient by giving the patient the right of informed consent. He is to fulfill his traditional role as healer and protector of the patient's life. There is extensive data on the healing that is possible within a trusting and caring doctor patient relationship.

Healing

Over the last three decades, a huge body of scientific and clinical evidence has emerged that demonstrates the importance of spiritual factors in physical healing. More and more medical research now concentrates on the complex relationship between mind, brain, endocrine and immune systems, as well as with spirit. Increasing numbers of patients are supplementing their medical treatment and well-being strategies with fitness, exercise, nutrition, meditation, prayer, faith, love, joy, psychological, and spiritual dimensions to enhance their health and lives.

In short, the best of science is being integrated with emotions, mental state, and spirituality. We find the origins of this contemporary pathway within the three thousand year old Bible. The Bible provides a wealth and depth of healing insights and medical anecdotes, which are more relevant than ever in this era's explosion of data and strategies on self-healing and well-being.

The Obligation to Heal

"Do not stand idly by the blood of your neighbor" (Leviticus 19:16). The obligation to heal is traditionally derived from Exodus 21:18-19: "And if two men fight, and one hits the other with a stone or his fist, and (the victim) does not die. . . (the aggressor) shall cause (the victim) to be thoroughly healed (that is, pay the physician's bill)." It naturally follows that if one must pay the doctor's bill, the physician must be allowed to treat the patient. Perhaps what was suggested here was actually an attempt to prevent the fighting in the first place. Perhaps one of the most beautiful passages in the Bible one day will find its reality in Isaiah 2:4: "He will judge between the nations and will settle disputes for many peoples. They will beat their swords into plowshares and their spears into pruning hooks. Nation will not take up sword against nation, nor will they train for war anymore."

Morality

"God's wisdom is as much above our wisdom as the heavens are above the earth" (Isaiah 55:8, 9); "God's understanding is infinite" (Psalms 147:5). In the Bible, morality is based upon respect for human life and all life (Genesis 9:6).

As the Greek philosophers suggested, a society is judged by how it treats its weakest members, even its animals. The Bible installed a remarkable code of ethics even for animals some 3,000 years ago. This was long before the ASCPA was inaugurated in 1866, when it was the most modern animal rights organization in the United States. In Deuteronomy 25:4, we find: "No muzzle on an ox as it threatens to deprive it of food while it is working." Leviticus 22:28 prohibits the slaughtering of an animal and its offspring on the same day; Genesis 9:4 prohibits the cruelty of cutting the limb off a live animal. Another well-known statute from the Bible is found in Deuteronomy 22:6-7 with the requirement to release a mother bird from her nest before removing her young.

In Exodus 24:14, we read of Rebecca, who brought water to the camels of Abraham's servant Eliezer. For this kind act, Eliezer decided that she was the right wife for Abraham's son Isaac. In Exodus 23:2, it states that even animals must have a day of rest: ". . . that the ox and thine ass may rest." How much more evidence do we need to understand the importance of the ethos we must show to one another when we recognize that we are required to have such respect for animals?

In the Talmud, it says that you must feed your animals and pets before yourself; and if an animal is in pain, you can bypass certain Sabbath restrictions to care for that animal. Also in Exodus 21:33, we find: "If a man uncovers a pit or digs one and fails to cover it and an ox or a donkey falls into it, the owner of the pit must pay for the loss.. Gandhi also concurred with this attitude when he said: "The greatness of a nation can be judged by the way its animals are treated."

Protecting the Environment

The Bible, as previously mentioned, has compassionate and ethical rulings for animals; but the Bible is also the first written source about conservation and being environmentally-friendly. In other words, the Bible was the first book to go "green."

Genesis 1:12 reads: "The earth brought forth vegetation, plants yielding seed after their kind, and trees . . ." And Deuteronomy 20:19 states: "When you besiege a city a long time, to make war against it in order to capture it, you shall not destroy its trees by swinging an axe against them; for you may eat from them, and you shall not cut them down . . ."

Environmental Sustainability

The Bible is also eco-friendly to the land in order to preserve it and make it more fertile. In Ezekiel 17:5-6 we read: "He also took some of the seed of the land and planted it in fertile soil. He placed it beside abundant waters; he set it like a willow. Then it sprouted and became a low, spreading vine with its branches turned toward him, but its roots remained under it. So it became a vine and yielded shoots and sent out branches."

Serving as an instruction book on how and when to toil the land, the Bible could almost be said to have provided for the first "Earth Day" holiday with Tu b'Shevat (the 15th day of the Hebrew month of Shevat), which is celebrated by the planting of trees and by eating locally grown fruits.

There are other biblical references to trees and their produce. For example, Genesis 2:5– 6: "Now all the trees of the field were not yet on the earth, and all the herbs of the field had not yet sprouted; for God had not sent rain upon the earth and there was no man to work the soil. A mist ascended from the earth and watered the whole surface of the soil. And God formed the man of dust from the ground . . ." Also, Leviticus 19:23: "When you enter the land and plant various kinds of fruit trees, you are to regard its fruit as forbidden; for three years it will be forbidden to you and not eaten . . ." And Leviticus 25:1-5: "Speak to the Children of Israel, and say to them, 'When you come into the land which I give you, then the land shall keep a Sabbath to the Lord. Six years you shall sow your field, and six years you shall prune your vineyard, and gather in its fruit; but in the seventh year, there shall be a Sabbath of solemn rest for the land, a Sabbath to the Lord. You shall neither sow your field nor prune your vineyard. What grows of its own accord of your harvest you shall not reap, nor gather the grapes of your untended vine, for it is a year of rest for the land.'"

Sustainability of the planet, after all, is about protecting human life.

Ethics and Responsible Practice

Medical ethics may acknowledge that God is the Creator and Sustainer of life (Genesis 1:27), and recognize that man is unique, made in the image of God (Genesis 1:27). The development of Medical ethical practices may also be formulated on secular and philosophical origins. Yet the sanctity of life is always central.

Today it is hardly a debate about whether or not one is permitted to donate his organs to save another life. But physicians are now faced with more challenges than ever before. These challenges have arisen, in part, because of the great strides that have been made in the medical field. In some instances, physicians are able to keep the body alive after the brain is dead. In other circumstances, they are able to keep the body alive, but only with the aid of ventilators (breathing machines), feeding tubes, intravenous feeding, and sophisticated equipment.

Challenges have been borne, in part, due to the secularization of society—a society that has legalized abortion; a society that, in time, will probably legalize euthanasia; a society that is thinking more favorably about cloning; and a society in which many are clamoring for stem-cell research, including the use of embryonic stem cells in which life is produced and then destroyed in order to produce body parts for the ill. From a Biblical-Judeo perspective many of these issues are indeed permissible within a framework of responsible conduct and rabbinic debate in certain circumstances.

Medical Dilemmas

Responsible medical practice today is faced with a spate of ethical problems. Many of these are generated by rapidly emerging biotechnology and by their nature these problems challenge our understanding of human nature and the practice of medicine.

A number of biblical principles might be considered in dealing with current medical dilemmas. Creation ethics and creation theology, which appear in Genesis and in other books of the Bible, bring out several relevant principles. Creation is seen as good and orderly (Genesis 1:31); humanity is created in the image of God. Our personhood is not dependent on biological integrity, or on our contribution to society, but on being made in the image of God. God created three basic classes of life, each class reproducing after its own kind—plants, animals, and people (Genesis 1:11, 12, 20–25, 26–30; 5:1–5).

The in vitro fertilization (IVF) topic spans the spectrum of issues regarding couples in a stable family relationship, but also from disparate sources of ovum and sperm and by the use of surrogacy. Within biblical and rabbinic law many of these issues continue to be expanded and discussed, allowing us to understand that the Bible is dynamic and relevant even in our modern age.

The Biblical View of Euthanasia

Perhaps the first recorded known use of euthanasia is discussed in relation to King Saul (II Samuel 1:6–10) when a young man told him: "By chance I happened to be on Mount Gilboa, and there was Saul leaning on his spear, and behold, the chariots and the horsemen were close upon him. And when he looked behind him, he saw me, and called to me. And I answered, 'Here I am.' And he said to me, 'Who are you?' I answered him, 'I am an Amalekite.' And he said to me 'Stand beside me and kill me, for anguish has seized me, and yet my life still lingers.' So I stood beside him and killed him, because I was sure that he could not live after he had fallen. And I took the crown that was on his head and the armlet that was on his arm, and I have brought them here to my lord." His lord, of course, was the future King David.

An example against killing oneself is shared by the Talmudic scholar Dr. Fred Rosner: The story of Rabbi Chanina ben Teradion (Avodah Zarah 18a), who was wrapped by the Romans in a Scroll of the Law (Torah) with bundles of straw around him that were set on fire. The Romans also put tufts of wool that had been soaked in water over his heart, so that he should not die quickly. His disciples pleaded with him to open his mouth "so that the fire (would) enter into thee" and put an end to his agony. He replied: "Let Him Who gave me (my soul) take it away." No one, however, is allowed to injure himself or hasten his death.

Another paradigm comes from the period when, in 73 C.E., the Romans laid siege to Masada—the last holdout of the Jewish zealots (as we previously cited). Reportedly, 960 of them decided to kill themselves rather than be taken as slaves and abused in ways too difficult to imagine. So it was decided that ten men would draw coins (lots) with the names of those who would kill the remaining survivors. Then, the very last one of them would kill himself; so theoretically, he would be the only one to actually commit suicide. The man chosen to commit that final act was probably their leader, Elazar ben Yair, whose speech at the top of Masada is still repeated to this day.

> "Since we long ago resolved never to be servants to the Romans, nor to any other than to God Himself, Who alone is the true and just Lord of mankind, the time is now come that obliges us to make that resolution true in practice. . . . We were the very first that revolted, and we are the last to fight against them; and I cannot but esteem it as a favor that God has granted us, that it is still in our power to die bravely, and in a state of freedom."

There is much medical debate regarding passive euthanasia often discussed in relation to prolonging undue suffering and thereby prolonging life in a terminally ill patient. Each situation is different and requires discussion, yet biblical law may allow for some forms of passive euthanasia.

So where is the philosophical cutoff of euthanasia? Is it before something painful occurs physically or mentally, or after the pain becomes too difficult to deal with? We are mere mortals, but we are created in the image of God; thus, that image is not founded just in a moral perspective, but, we hope, in wisdom as well. Should the decision about ending life be left to governments? In the United States today only four states—Washington, Oregon, Montana, and Vermont permit physician-assisted dying (PAD). In Europe, Switzerland has allowed it since the 1940s but the Netherlands, Belgium, and Luxembourg also permit it. In 2012, Luxembourg only had 14 such deaths, while in the Netherlands, there were more than 3.500 of them.

On a personal level, I watched for almost seven years as my mother, Leni Kash, suffered with double-hip replacement and double-knee replacement, then due to Type 2 diabetes; ultimately, both her legs were amputated. She was extremely courageous during an entire five years when she was almost never pain-free. My father, then in his eighties, would carry her, bathe her, and care for her. During the last year, she pleaded with my father and me in earnest to help her die because she couldn't do it herself. Were we selfish in not assisting her? I think about this almost every day. I am glad that we didn't have to take the course of assisted suicide, but I understand the difficult decisions so many people have to go through as they watch love ones suffer.

We as individuals, and as family members, have to make decisions about ourselves or about our loved ones who become terminally ill, decisions that may involve either passive or active euthanasia. We also need to make decisions regarding IVF and possibly the use of stem cells, and from whence those stem cells are harvested. The choices often prompt more questions than answers, but if we delve deeply, the Bible offers much wisdom that can help us in times of agonizing decisions.

Chapter 9

The Future of Medicine— Becoming God?

Future Science

As with any living organism, we humans learn, we adapt, and we build upon the previous generation; and it all gets wired and imbedded into our DNA and is passed unto the next generation. Revolutionary new technology, new patents, and new science are constantly unfolding.

There are many areas of incredible scientific advances such as neuroscience and neuroplasticity, telomeres and longevity, the human genome and epigenetics, and, of course, the huge field of stem cell research. We will examine just one or two of these advances.

The Hidden Source

Perhaps the least well-known holiday celebrated by the Jewish people is Purim, the Festival of Lots, which dates back to the year 357 B.C.E. Haman, a despot of ancient Persia, sought to destroy the Jewish people, and through myriad circumstances, the Jewish people are saved. What is interesting is that God is never mentioned in the story of Purim, which was written in the Scroll of Esther and is read twice, on the festival.

Like the story of Purim, God is mostly hidden within scientific breakthroughs. Regardless of your belief system, as you read the

Bible, stroll on the beach, or look up at the sky, it is hard to imagine that everything was caused by spontaneous mutations. The authors contend— (although you, the reader may not hold the same belief)—that we are indeed created in God's image. If so, why not in His intellect as well? Genesis 1:26-27 reveals, "Then God said, 'Let us make man in our image, in our likeness' . . . So God created man in His own image, in the image of God He created him; male and female he created them."

Stem Cell Research

Stem cell research is transforming the future of medicine. Indeed, we all begin life as a stem cell, and it is through a highly complex series of events that those few stem cells, which are capable of self-renewal and differentiation, develop into all of the specialized cells found in our adult bodies. By studying these events, we gain rare insights into how the human body is made.

Stem cell research also holds amazing potential for restructuring the way we practice medicine. One day, stem cells will be used to replace or repair damaged tissues and organs and to dramatically alter how we treat diseases such as cancer. There are many areas in medicine in which stem cell research could have a significant impact. As was said in the Bible (Jeremiah 1:4-5): "Now the word of the Lord came to me, saying, 'Before I formed you in the womb I knew you, and before you were born I consecrated you; I appointed you a prophet to the nations.'"

For example, there are a variety of diseases and injuries in which a patient's cells or tissues are destroyed and must be replaced by tissue or organ transplants. Stem cells may be able to generate brand new tissue in these cases, and even cure diseases for which there currently is no adequate therapy. Diseases that could see revolutionary advances include Alzheimer's and Parkinson's disease, diabetes, spinal cord injury, heart disease, stroke, arthritis, cancer, burns, and regeneration of spinal cord cells. Various laboratories are working on the remarkable science of "reprograming" stem cells for potential organ transplants.

Stem cells could also be used to gain a better understanding of how genetics work in the early stages of cell development. This can help scientists understand why some cells develop abnormally and lead to medical problems, such as birth defects and cancer. By understanding the genetic basis for cell development, scientists may learn how to prevent some of these diseases.

In addition, stem cells may be useful in the testing and development of drugs. Because stem cells can be used to create unlimited amounts of specialized tissue, such as heart tissue, it may be possible to test how drugs react on these specialized tissues before trying the drugs on animals and human subjects. Drugs could be tested for effectiveness and side effects more rapidly.

Others are exploring how stem cells contribute to diseases in order to develop ways to improve conventional treatment and prevention of these disorders.

Mini Brains

Another glimpse into the future occurred in the recent past when it was announced that the first complete living model of the developing human brain had been created in a lab dish by researchers headed by Jüergen Knoblich, of the Austrian Academy of Science's Institute of Molecular Biotechnology in Vienna. These so-called mini-brains will allow more drugs to be developed to treat and ultimately cure many of the brain disorders that affect millions of patients worldwide.

New Blood Vessels

Another pioneer in the area of adult stem cell research is Romanian-born, Australian-educated Dr. Silvio Itescu, who established Angioblast Systems in 2001, and later Mesoblast, the largest adult stem cell company in the world. The firm's research has a specific focus on the development and commercialization of novel therapeutic products for the treatment of cardiovascular diseases and vascular disorders. Dr. Itescu had previously worked as the Head of Transplantation Immunology at Columbia University Medical Center; he was truly the first pioneer with data that showed he could regenerate heart tissue and form new blood vessels to improve the heart's blood supply. He originally specialized in the field of immunosuppressants to prevent the rejection of transplanted organs. It is expected that in the not-too-distant future, stem cell technology will inevitably allow us to grow and harvest heart tissue.

People wonder why science takes so long; well, the first two truly identified pioneers of stem cell research began their work more than 50 years ago. On February 1, 1961, Dr. James Till and Dr. Ernest McCulloch of Toronto published findings on radiation research that proved the existence of stem cells, showing that these unique cells could regenerate themselves and be used for myriad medical purposes. At the time, they couldn't have envisioned where their discovery would lead.

Personalization: From Genomics to Proteomics

It has already been a decade since the huge revolutionary development of sequencing the entire human genome: This understanding of the entire genetic profile of a human cost billions of dollars. Numerous companies such as *23andMe* are now offering partial DNA genotyping to discover your hereditary roots from thousands of years ago, potential future health issues that are genetically based, personality traits, and so forth. What would have cost you thousands of dollars a few years ago, costs less than $100 today. This means it is now becoming more affordable to compare one person's DNA with another's, learn what diseases those with similar genetics have had, and discover how effective different medications or other interventions were in treating them. Imagine doing a Google search on specific genes to find others like you and learn their abilities, allergies, likes and dislikes, and what diseases they are predisposed to suffer from. That future is closer than you may think.

This opens up an era of crowd-sourced, data-driven, participatory, genomics-based medicine. Today, medicines are prescribed on a "one-size-fits-all" basis. When a particular medication causes a significant negative reaction with a small part of the population, it is prevented from being available to anyone. In the future, expect to see doctors prescribing and selecting the most patient-appropriate medicines based on a person's DNA (the field of "pharmacogenomics").

Regenerative Medicine

King Solomon wisely stated in Ecclesiastes 1:9, "What has been will be again, what has been done will be done again; there is nothing new under the sun."

In a new frontier, such as regenerative medicine, longstanding ethical issues resurface with fresh significance. The journey from exciting scientific breakthrough to routine medical procedure passes through the phases of clinical research trials. In the first stage of clinical research, Phase I trials, researchers test a new treatment on a small group of patients to evaluate if the treatment is safe and to discover possible side effects. Physicians have been conducting adult stem cell therapy for more than 40 years in the field of bone marrow transplantation, which involves transplanting stem cells that become red blood cells. Adult stem cells are now being applied in a variety of arenas, from orthopedics to cardiovascular therapy. The first trials using cells derived from embryonic stem cells were for acute spinal cord injury and started within the last year. But embryonic stem cells have raised ethical and moral controversies, even though the research remains critical for future progress.

Creation of Organs: From Dream to Reality

The artificial generation of tissues, organs, or even more complex living organisms was, throughout the history of mankind, a matter of myth and dream. During the last decades, this vision has become feasible and has been recently introduced in clinical medicine. Tissue engineering and regenerative medicine are terms for the field in biomedicine that deal with the transformation of these fundamental ideas to practical approaches. Several aspects of generating new tissues and organs out of small pieces of living specimens are now scientifically solved, but at this point, it is unknown how much impact these new approaches will have on clinical medicine in the future. In this respect it seems important to recapitulate from where the visions and the work came, in order to speculate or predict where tissue engineering and regenerative medicine will head.

Creation of Eve from Adam's Rib

The concept of tissue engineering and regenerative medicine as measures to create more complex organisms from simpler pieces is deeply embedded in the people's imaginary world. Reference Genesis 2:21: "And the Lord God caused a deep sleep to fall upon Adam, and he slept: and he took one of his ribs, and closed up the flesh instead thereof; Genesis 2:22: "And the rib, which the Lord God had taken from man, made he a woman, and brought her unto the man." The biblical tale of Eve created from Adam's rib is perhaps the most well-known example of the concept of creation of a complex being from a part (in a modern view, a kind of hybrid cloning). A multitude of examples in literature and the arts mirrors the desire of humans to be able to create *by themselves* living individuals or at least parts of individuals. A change in the vision, hope, and belief of how to create or regenerate complex organs or organisms can be observed during history as a mirror of the cultural history of mankind. Even the early history of mankind is related to the idea that independent life can be created without sexual reproduction. Stories from Greek mythology (the creation of persons without sexual reproduction, such as the generation of Prometheus) may be considered as early reports representing the idea of creating living creatures from living or nonliving specimens. The envisioned measures to create life are influenced by the social, cultural, and scientific background of individual persons at that time.

As humans progressed in the understanding of nature, and as they developed more advanced culture techniques, they envisioned the generation of living creatures by applying physicochemical or biological techniques. During the transformation from the Middle Ages to the Renaissance in Europe, there was the hope and belief by a number of scientists that, through alchemy, living organisms could be generated. Theophrastus von Hohenheim—better known as Paracelsus—tried (and failed) to find a recipe to create human life by a mixture of chemical substances in a defined environment.

Goethe's *Faust*: Creating Man

Johann Wolfgang von Goethe (1749–1832) deals in his fundamental work of literature, *Faust*, with the relation of an individual (Faust) to knowledge, power, morality, and theology. One central theme in the struggle of Faust to be powerful is the deeply embedded wish to create life. The creation of the artificial being Homunculus becomes a central part of the drama, by which Goethe reveals various transformational processes working in the human soul. In the famous laboratory scene of *Faust*, he describes the vision of men being able to create life by alchemy, representing the irrepressible human dream of "engineering" life:

"Look there's a gleam!—Now hope may be fulfilled,
That hundreds of ingredients, mixed, distilled—
And mixing is the secret—give us power
The stuff of human nature to compound
If in a limbeck we now seal it round
And cohobate with final care profound,
The finished work may crown this silent hour."

There are many contemporary "Faustian" technologies, such as cloning, genetic, or stem cell techniques in modern tissue engineering and regenerative medicine. With respect to a historical view of tissue engineering, Faust is a representative of Northern European humanity striving for evolution from the scientific and ethical limitations and strictures of the 16th-century Reformation Era to the new aspirations of humanity that Goethe saw developing during the 18th-century Age of Enlightenment. He was attracted to the idea of creating life by adding substances to nonliving specimens, similar to visions of how God created Adam, visualized by the famous painting of Michelangelo. Goethe seemed to struggle to weave the personal inner journey of Faust toward some enlightenment when he wrote: "I've studied now Philosophy, and Jurisprudence, Medicine, and even alas! Theology All through and through with ardour keen! Here now I stand, poor fool, and see I'm just as wise as formerly. Am called a Master, even Doctor too, And now I've nearly ten years through Pulled my students by their noses to and fro And up and down, across, about, And see there's nothing we can know!"

The context is the collective social forces that are undergoing transformation through the historical processes of that time. As Faust deals with nearly all aspects and questions that arise in tissue engineering and regenerative medicine, it can be considered to be a timeless and always relevant consideration on the field of biomedicine. Later, as science and medicine progressed, a multitude of stories, reports, paintings, and films dealt with the idea that humans could create life by modern "scientific" measures.

Mary Shelley's *Frankenstein*

A prominent newer example in literature and film is the story of Frankenstein, written by Mary Shelley in 1818, describing the vitalization of a creature that was reassembled from different body parts. Parallel to the mythological, biblical, and fictional reports, various persons performed pioneering practical work to generate, heal, or regenerate body parts. The emergence of tissue engineering is, through their work, closely connected with the development of clinical medicine (prosthetics, reconstructive surgery, transplantation medicine, and microsurgery) and biology (cell biology, biochemistry, molecular biology, genetics).

Prosthetics and Reconstruction

The mechanical substitution of body parts by non-vital prosthetic devices such as metallic and ivory dentures and wooden legs

can be considered as early efforts to use biomaterials in reconstructive medicine. The first attempts to replace teeth in the sense
of modern dental implantology seems to go back as early as in
the Galileo-Roman period. The anthroposophic finding of a human skull, containing a metallic implant in the jaw, is indicative of
early attempts of humans to regain lost function by tissue substitution. Leading areas of reconstructive medicine in clinical use
were evident in the age before modern dentistry and orthopedics.
Ambroise Paré (1510–1590) described in his work *Dix livres de la
chirurgie* measures to reconstruct teeth, noses, and other parts of
the body.

Tissue Engineering

The term "tissue engineering" as it is nowadays used was introduced in medicine in 1987. The definition that was agreed on
was: "Tissue Engineering is the application of the principles and
methods of engineering life sciences toward the fundamental understanding of structure-function relationships in normal and
pathologic mammalian tissue and the development of biological
substitutes to restore, maintain, or improve function."

The early years of tissue engineering were based on cell and
tissue culture approaches. John F. Burke and Ioannis Yannas made
significant innovations in this approach through a laboratory and
clinical collaboration between Massachusetts General Hospital in
Boston and Massachusetts Institute of Technology in Cambridge.
They were aimed at generating synthetic skin by a culture of der-
mal fibroblasts or keratinocytes on protein scaffolds, and using it
for the regeneration of burn wounds. A key point in tissue engineering was given by the close cooperation between Dr. Joseph
Vacanti from Boston Children's Hospital and Dr. Robert Langer
from M.I.T. Their 1993 article in *Science* 266, describing the new
technology may be considered the beginning of this new biomedical discipline. Later, a large number of centers all over the world
focused their research efforts toward this field.

Tissue engineering was catapulted to the forefront of the public awareness with a BBC broadcast "Exploring the Potential of Tissue-engineered Cartilage," which included images of the now infamous "mouse with the human ear" on its back from the laboratory of Dr. Charles Vacanti at the University of Massachusetts Medical Center. The visual power of the photograph of the "auriculosaurus" helped transfer the idea and vision of generating new tissues or organs from the imaginary world of human beings to the real world. Since that time, tissue engineering has been considered one of the most promising biomedical technologies of the century.

Regenerative Medicine

Regenerative medicine seems to be more difficult to define; this term was used earlier but was less defined in the literature than the term "tissue engineering." Nevertheless, most biologists and physicists now viewed it as a field where stem cells drive embryonic formation, or where inductive organizers induce a blastema to regenerate a tissue, aimed at reforming damaged tissues and organs in humans. It seems that a rigid definition of regenerative medicine is not constructive, while the principle approaches that define the field are still being delineated. Stem cells being stem cells, being at the center of expectations, hold great promise for the future of regenerative medicine. Stem cell plasticity and cloning, with nuclear transfer, transdifferentiation, and cell fusion as measures to modulate the stem cell differentiation pathway, are now central issues in regenerative medicine.

"We think we can do it in ten years — that we can build, from a patient's own cells, a total 'bioficial heart'," said Dr. Stuart Williams, executive and scientific director of the Cardiovascular Innovation Institute. The institute hopes to advance adult stem cell research in treatment of heart disease so that within ten-plus years scientists will be able to generate the bioficial heart from a patient's own cardiac stem cells known as "c-kit positive" cells. The implications of this are also due to a new field known as 3-D bio-printing that will allow copies of various organs from hearts to liver, kidneys, and so forth.

Regeneration holds the hope that may propel humans to live beyond our wildest imaginations—so far from the first example of Eve's being born from Adam's rib. Yet philosophically and spiritually one has to ask its purpose. It takes us to the core of existential questioning: Why all this knowledge and why now? Where is it taking us? The 1977 movie *Close Encounters of the Third Kind*, directed by Steven Spielberg, showed people who were affected by an alien light of some sort had an urge to get to the mountaintop known as Devils Tower in Wyoming; is it possible that we humans are touched in such a way, perhaps even pre-programmed to get to some destination as the myriads of other intelligent life forms that are separated by thousands of years traveling at the speed of light and that only a few actually make it? We might only ever know the answer through regeneration, cloning, and other technologies not yet developed.

The Bible guides us in this direction by saying, "My son, do not forget my teaching, but keep my commands in your heart, for they will prolong your life many years and bring you prosperity . . . This will bring health to your body and nourishment to your bones" (Proverbs 3:1–2,8).

Organ Transplantation

Organ transplantation has made tremendous strides in the past 50 years and will continue with better and improved outcomes.

From the earliest days of the Bible, mankind was to demonstrate a love for God as well as for his neighbors. Being willing to donate an organ from our own bodies would seem to be an extreme example of selfless sacrifice for another. "If you listen carefully to the voice of the Lord your God and do what is right in his eyes, if you pay attention to his commands and keep all his decrees, I will not bring on you any of the diseases I brought on the Egyptians, for I am the Lord, who heals you" (Exodus 15:26).

Potential Technological Advances in the Future of Medicine

The projects with the biggest potential to be used in everyday medical practice—and which advance not only longevity but also the quality of life—will help determine the future of medicine.

Ray Kurzweil, a futurist, inventor, and Director of Research at Google believes as we do that in the near future (2020) through the use of genomics, we will be able to program and tailor-make targeted drugs and thereby simply have the ability to program or reprogram our biology. Synthetic DNA is being developed that will potentially fool and eradicate viruses. Nano-technology and nano-robots will be roaming our bodies one day, monitoring our health and destroying mutant cells before they have a chance to replicate.

Here are several other examples of technological advances that will most likely affect the future of medicine:

1. Switching from long and extremely expensive clinical trials to tiny microchips that can be used as models of human organs or whole physiological systems will provide clear advantages.
2. Medical students will study anatomy on virtual dissection tables, not on human cadavers. We can observe, change, and create anatomical models as fast as we want, as well as analyze structures in every detail.
3. With the growing number of elderly patients, introducing robot assistants to patient care homes and hospitals is inevitable. It could be a fair solution to problems of moving patients or performing basic procedures.
4. Today FitBits and other devices measure easily quantifiable data, but the future belongs to digestible and wearable sensors that can work in and on the body. These sensors may measure all important health parameters and vital signs from temperature and blood biomarkers to neurological symptoms 24 hours a day, transmitting data to the cloud and sending alerts to medical systems when a stroke is hap-

pening in real time. It may call the ambulance itself and
send all the related data immediately.

5. IBM Watson will assist physicians in everyday medical de-
cision-making, although it will not substitute for humans
at all. While a physician can follow a few dozens of papers
with digital solutions, Watson can process more than 200
million pages in three seconds; therefore, with the increasing amount of scientific data, it would be a wise decision
to use this tool in the practice of medicine.

6. Since the completion of the Human Genome Project, we
have been envisioning the era of personalized medicine in
which everyone gets customized therapy with customized
dosages. The truth is that there are only about 30 cases
when personal genomics can be applied with evidence in
the background according to the Personalized Medicine
Coalition. As we move along, there will be more and more
opportunities to use DNA analysis at the patient's bedside,
which should be a must-have before actually prescribing
drugs.

7. In the near future, all medical information will simply be
available to each and every one of us. With information
readily available, perhaps, on a daily basis—from cholesterol levels to deficiency in vitamin B levels to surges in
cortisol levels—it will be collected and monitored on nan-
ochips, which may even travel freely throughout your body
by using wireless communication. Before you think this is
unrealistic, just look at what Given Imaging accomplished
with a camera in a pill that is swallowed; the idea was sold
for $860 million.

8. If guns and other objects are being printed now, and the
biotechnology industry is working on printing even living
cells, why would the appearance of 3D printed drugs be
surprising? It will destroy and redesign the whole pharma-
ceutical world. Regulation, however, will be a huge chal-

lenge, because anyone will be able to print any kind of drug that contains patented molecules at home.

9. Adherence and compliance represent crucial issues in improving patients' health and decreasing the cost of delivering healthcare. Several start-ups have targeted this issue with different solutions, such as a pill bottle that glows blue when a medication dose should be taken and red when a dose is missed (winner of the recent Healthcare Innovation World Cup); or tiny digestible sensors that can be placed in pills and can transmit pill digestion data to physicians and family members. In the future, it's going to be extremely difficult to conceal information from your doctor.

You're Unique

Even though you're special, today's medical treatment is still generic. Today, your physician would run diagnostic tests, compare your current health and test results to that of a typical human of your age and gender, and treat your disease accordingly. Therein is the problem. You are custom made, with a unique combination of lifestyle, environment, exercise patterns, and food preferences. Although your nominal genetic profile is determined at conception, which genes are expressed (turned on) varies across organs and even with lifestyle and diet. Hence, it is not surprising that your reactions to a medical treatment may be quite different from another individual with the same test results.

P4 Medicine

A one-size-fits-all approach to medicine is about to change. What biologist Leroy Hood has called P4 Medicine—predictive, preventive, personalized, and participatory—is tantalizingly near. The building blocks of that future provide a deeper understanding of biological processes and continued advances in mobile sensors and big data analytics. Let's imagine the future, one where you really are special. Your physician will compare your current health to the best possible baseline. That would be you, but you in the best physical and mental condition of your life. Perhaps you were 25, at your optimum weight, exercising regularly, getting plenty of sleep, and eating a well-balanced diet. Your physician would then tailor your treatment based on a detailed understanding of your genetic profile and gene expression, your current lifestyle and environment, and your body's specific reactions to the prescribed treatment.

Continued advances in microfluidics, nanotechnology, microelectronics, and robotics are rapidly reducing the cost of genome sequencing and metabolic characterization. Just a decade ago, the Human Genome Project spent over $3 billion to sequence one genome. Dr. Craig Venter is credited along with Dr. Francis Collins of the National Institutes of Health (NIH) with unraveling the human genome sequence in the year 2000. Today, that same process costs just a few thousand dollars. In a few years, sequencing and metabolic analysis will be a routine diagnostic test, costing just few hundred dollars. Everyone will know how their biological engine is working, and how it compares to that magical time when they were 25. In a few years, sequencing and metabolic analysis will be a routine diagnostic test costing just few hundred dollars.

This will be great news if you are sick. The real trick is keeping you healthy, eliminating the need for many treatments by predicting disease, and intervening to prevent it. The key is to detect subtle changes in gene expression and metabolism before they manifest as illness. Your biochemistry tells the tale before you feel sick.

Bionic Man

Since 2010, Dr. Venter has patented the first synthetic biological organism by transplanting manmade DNA into a bacterial cell. This is more than just Frankenstein science fiction; this is a peek into a brave, new world. You may remember the first hint of the future in 1974 with the hit TV series the *Six Million Dollar Man*, played by Lee Majors; after his character suffers a crash as an astronaut, they rebuild him with two "bionic" legs, arm, and eye. Today it is not so farfetched; Israeli and American companies are now creating Exo-Skeletons that allow paraplegics to walk independently for the first time. Until such time that nano-implants and spinal regeneration with stem cells is feasible, these futuristic devices are here today, giving dignity and hope to challenged patient and their loved ones.

Thirty years ago, we depended on dashboard gauges, red lights, dripping fluids, and strange noises to alert us to vehicle problems. Today, all vehicles have on-board diagnostics that continuously monitor mechanical and electrical systems, comparing their current state to the factory norm. Those same diagnostic systems alert the owner of impending problems and routine maintenance and provide a detailed history for repair. Don't you deserve at least the same early, unobtrusive warnings about your health?

Mind Boggling

A combination of technologies based on nano-materials, microfluidics, semiconductors, and wireless sensors will bring inexpensive, real-time monitoring to personal healthcare by regularly comparing an individual's current metabolic state to his or her personal optimum. Stripping away the technical jargon, it means that each of us may have wearable and perhaps implantable metabolic diagnostics that will provide us with a better early health warning system than nature gave us. The consumerization of IT will drive the final, sweeping changes in participatory healthcare. Smartphone apps that measure lung function by listening to breathing and that assess blood pressure and heart rate via cameras are just the first wave. The emerging Internet of Things—ubiquitous, inexpensive, wireless sensors that unobtrusively capture environmental, behavioral, and physiological data—will provide lifestyle context that complements on-board medical diagnostics. The *Star Trek* tricorder is in sight.

There is a famous economic cycle called the Kondratiev Cycle, which basically demonstrates that the world goes into macro recessions and depression every 52-60 years or so; but the way out is with new technology that causes consumption; well, the next technological wave is the combination of biology and physics that will mind-boggle even the greatest visionaries and dreamers.

The combination of data analytics, lifestyle sensor data, and metabolic diagnostics may let aging seniors live healthy, independent lives for far longer, help everyone balance lifestyle choices and genetic health risks, and schedule preventive healthcare based on early warning signs. Equally important, it will empower individuals to manage their own health, working in partnerships with healthcare providers.

Despite all this sci-fi technology, it is still important to listen to your mother, respect others, eat your vegetables, and wash your hands!

The War on Cancer

Believe it or not the war on cancer started thousands of years ago. Hippocrates came up with the origin of the word 'Karkinos' meaning crablike or spreading, as cancer so often tragically does. There is actual data written on papyrus some 3,500 years ago in ancient Egypt that depict efforts to heat the cancer in order to try and kill it with a hot instrument.

The first recognized chemotherapy agents were designed from World War I and World War II chemical agents. Dr. Paul Erlich, who won the Nobel Prize for developing Salvarsan for treating syphilis, also coined the word "chemotherapy" from his work. Ultimately, he also worked on cancer research. Later, Dr. Sydney Farber of Harvard University, the noted oncologist who is considered the father of modern chemotherapy and for whom the Dana Farber Institute in Boston is named, first used Aminpoterin to treat a form of pediatric leukemia, known as acute lymphatic leukemia, discovered by Dr. Yellapragada Subbarao, also from Harvard. The war on cancer began and is still ongoing.

Albert and Mary Lasker changed the scope of the effort by creating the first major donation to fund medical research and the war on cancer in 1946; each year since, recipients receive generous financial awards for their research; eighty-three recipients of the

Lasker Award have gone on to win the Nobel Prize. Albert Lasker, who was considered the "father of modern advertising," wanted a way to give back to the country that gave his family the life they enjoyed after his father witnessed anti-Semitism in Prussia. In 1946, his wife Mary helped foster the beginning of the National Cancer Institute.

In 1971, President Richard Nixon's signed the original National Cancer Act that declared the "War on Cancer." In 2012, the research budget of the National Institute of Health reached close to $30.7 billion; $5.6 billion of that went to the National Cancer Institute. That money was divided among 2,500 universities, 6,000 NIH scientists, and more than 300,000 research projects. In addition, the funds were combined with close to $50 billion from private pharmaceutical and biotech companies for research into new medicines. The results have produced close to 1,000 new therapies and vaccines in development to treat, prevent, and cure cancer, which, along with the approximately 2,300 current agents in the medicine cabinet of doctors today, are helping us get closer to controlling and eradicating most cancers.

The Tree of Knowledge; The Tree of Healing

"From any tree of the garden you may eat freely; but from the Tree of Knowledge of good and evil you shall not eat, for in the day that you eat from it you will surely die" (Genesis 2:17).

It is fascinating that several drugs and hundreds of herbal medicines actually come from trees and plants. Many highly potent drugs for cancer have come from trees, like Taxol, which was first approved in 1992, but was discovered from the Pacific yew tree in the American Northwest as early as August 21, 1962 when botanists were unleashed by the Cancer Chemotherapy National Service to find possible agents in nature to fight against cancer. Two years later, in 1964, it was determined that Paclitaxel could be an active agent, and 28 years later the drug started to be used to treat a variety of cancers including lung, breast, ovarian, head and neck, and so forth.

Today, trastuzumab-DM—a potential drug in the arsenal to fight breast and other cancers—has been found in evergreen trees. One of the more interesting recent drugs is called Combrestastatin, from the African bush willow tree; it reduces blood flow to starve off cancer cells. The originator of this theory, Dr. Judah Folkman, a son of a rabbi, believed that by choking off the blood supply you could starve cancer. This process became known as anti-angiogenesis, for which Dr. Folkman is considered the main pioneer.

Gene Therapy and Cancer

Who could have imagined thousands of years ago the transfer and manipulation of genes to correct illness and hereditary disorders? Although it has been some four decades since the original thoughts and visions about gene therapy by Dr. Richard Mulligan, we are still scratching the surface of the role of gene therapy for the future. In 1986, the first animal studies using gene therapy proved that it was possible to treat disease by conditioning the bone marrow; later, in 1989, the famous Dr. Steve Rosenberg from the NIH, formulized the concept of using gene therapy to fight melanoma. According to the Mayo Clinic in Minnesota, melanoma increased eightfold in women from 1970-2009 and fourfold in men. In Australia, one in 17 will be diagnosed with melanoma before the age of 85, making it the highest incidence in the world. How many readers can still remember using Aluminium foil in the 1960s and 70's to help get a deeper tan?

It wasn't until September 14, 1990 that Dr. W. French Anderson treated a patient with a deficiency in Adenosine Deaminase (ADA) by taking the patient's white blood cells and inserting ADA, thereby curing the patient of the deficiency. Even more amazing, in 2000, French doctors treated and cured ten children with X-SCID or Bubble Boy Syndrome; unfortunately two of the patients developed leukemia thereafter. Yet today this syndrome—which John Travolta depicted in the film "Boy in the Plastic Bubble" in 1976 and more recently was the topic in the *Seinfeld* episode in which George Costanza had a fight with the "Boy in the Bubble"—is curable.

The Future Is Around the Corner

In the future, gene therapy may not be used just to cure cancer, but to treat many other diseases, especially hereditary diseases. And that day is within reach. Treatment as early as in the fetal stage may be the future of eradicating or at least correcting hereditary diseases, including cystic fibrosis, thalassemia, sickle cell anemia, hemophilia, and Tay-Sachs.

But as research continues, the question is, are we playing God? We will leave the philosophical debate to others. Our goal is to share promise for those with cancer and incurable disease and instill hope for the very near future.

Vaccines and Cancer

The earliest known form of vaccines was the practice of variolation, which goes as far back as the 10th century in China. It was the practice to inoculate children, and even adults, with a weaker variation of the smallpox disease (which has genetic traits that date as far back as 10,000 years ago) that killed millions of Asians, Europeans, and Native American Indians. The Chinese and their Indian neighbors would blow a dried, smallpox scab into the nose of a person, thereby exposing him to the dreadful smallpox; data show that only one to two percent of those that were variolated died, compared to more than 30–50 percent who were exposed and contracted the disease at its peak strength. Eventually over the centuries, this practice became commonplace, even to the point of creating a puncture wound in which to introduce the weakened smallpox under the skin as was practiced in the West.

African slaves introduced variolation into America. In Massachusetts, Cotton Mather, who actually spoke Hebrew fluently, learned about the practice. Mather publicized the technique, and the procedure was first tried during a smallpox epidemic in Boston in 1721. The irony is that it was the knowledge of the slaves that saved the people of Boston and America at large.

Vaccines for cancer are just an extension of modern-day vaccines that were developed beginning in the 1930s for typhoid, diphtheria, tetanus, rubella, pertussis, mumps, chicken pox, polio, rotavirus, then hepatitis A and B. Today the first true prophylactic vaccine for cancer is the HPV vaccine against cervical cancer, which works effectively in cancer of the vagina, vulva, anus, and even head and neck, along with working against HPV 6 & 11 that is responsible for 90 percent of genital infections. Harald zur Hausen, a German researcher, worked for 10 years before proving that cervical cancer was caused by the Human Papilloma Virus. He was ultimately awarded the Nobel Prize for his discovery. Merck and GlaxoSmithKline launched Gardasil and Cervarix as vaccines in 2007 and 2008 respectively. The peace of mind that it brings parents is enormous, and the head and neck cancer prevention is mostly for men who can contract the virus, too.

The future of vaccines against cancer will be both prophylactic (preventive) and therapeutic (treating diagnosed patients). Most vaccines will help assist the B cells that create the antibodies to light up like a flare, thereby permitting the T cells (the commando cells) to actually destroy the cancer cells. So, from cervical cancer, to melanoma, lung, kidney, bone, liver, and the like, the war on cancer is now in our favor, as long as the funding and entrepreneurial environment stays alive, inspiring a new breed of scientists and researchers from around the world.

Alzheimer's Disease and the Bible

But is there anything on Alzheimer's from the Bible? In Psalms 137:5 we read: "If I forget you Jerusalem, let my right hand lose its strength. Let my tongue cling to my palate if I fail to recall you, if I fail to elevate Jerusalem above my highest joy." There is no direct link between this statement and dementia; but the concept of forgetting was always around. Each day, in fact, every hour, somewhere in the world someone new is getting some form of

Alzheimer's disease. Much global data reveals that about 36 million people live with Alzheimer's or some form of dementia, and each year another seven million join this club. When we look at the Bible and see some of the longevity spans, we wonder if there were forms of Alzheimer's, but with King David's simple and straightforward statement, "If I forget," it is clear that there has always been a great concern for memory and forgetting.

There is some preliminary evidence demonstrating a possible link between the chronic diseases of lifestyle such as obesity, diabetes, and heart disease with Alzheimer's. The ancient Israelites, like most people of biblical times, did not live sedentary lives: There is certainly a correlation between exercise, healthy eating, and the prevention of dementia and Alzheimer's. There are also many theories and a vast amount of ongoing research into this field, but unfortunately as yet, much more is unknown than understood about dementia.

Epilogue

What Have We Accomplished?

In writing this book, *Take Two Tablets*, it was our intention to introduce the reader to the wisdom and philosophies in the Bible that relate to health, both physically and spiritually. So, how do we conclude a book that relates to the Bible? The fact is that there can be no conclusion; the Bible is a tool, and like this book, it should be used to enhance your knowledge and, in turn, your practice. If you glean only one or two bits of new information, and if your newfound awareness transforms what you knew beforehand—regarding nutrition, dealing with stress, and recognizing who you were before reading this—then we have accomplished a great deal together.

Most importantly, we are tasked with the duty of continuity in educating our children and inspiring them with the wisdom of the Bible. The recipe for raising children with the Bible's teachings is found in Deuteronomy 6:7: "You shall teach them diligently to your children, and shall talk of them when you sit in your house, and when you walk by the way, and when you lie down, and when you rise." We are all so busy trying to manage so many aspects of our lives that we forget that the main recipe for raising children is right there in the Bible.

The ancient Hebrews derived their name not from God nor from Abraham or Moses, but from someone—a neighbor perhaps—who recognized that Abraham was different from others of his time, and so he called him an "Ivri," a Hebrew: "One who had escaped came and reported this to Abram the Hebrew" (Genesis 14:13). Etymologically speaking, the word "Ivri" means someone who has "crossed over a boundary"—a geographical physical location. However, one could argue that its meaning is much deeper, and this might be said of every word in the Bible, because the language of the Bible is not linear; it is necessary to unravel the root and to be aware of the context in order to grasp its full meaning.

In actuality, Abraham also crossed beyond the spiritual boundary of his birth, by not bowing down to stone statutes and going against the teachings of his father Terach. Other cultures around him were offering human sacrifices; but Abraham learned with the Binding of Isaac that God had no need for human sacrifices. It was, perhaps, God's intention to show Abraham and the world that to love God is the beginning of living a righteous life.

In fact, it could be said that the very name Israel ישראל is a code for three patriarchs and four matriarchs of the Jewish people: The yud, for Ya'akov (also called Yisrael); the sin, for Sarah; the resh, for Rivkah and Rachel; the alef for Avraham; and the lamed, for Leah. Indeed, there is no mathematical possibility that it could have been anything else, given the twenty-two letters in the Hebrew alphabet and the initials of Judaism's seven patriarchs and matriarchs. The likelihood that it would have been different is statistically in the billions. This leads us to the reality that the Bible is here for a purpose, as are we; it does not really matter whether you believe it was written by God Himself, by Moses, or by several other writers: We are not here to judge anyone's belief system. However, after five years of research, the evidence is substantial that whatever the Bible's source, it is replete with wisdom about human frailties and the delicacy of human nature.

Take Two Tablets is about how to make ourselves healthier, both medically and spiritually. It is about us as individuals and collectively as the human race. We have to consider all the implications for our purpose in being here. Perhaps we haven't evolved enough yet to fully contemplate the power given to us to make advancements and change from stem cells to robotic parts for our bodies, synthetic skin, or nano computer chips, but make no mistake about it—it is not by mistake that we are here.

One of our favorite authors is MIT-educated physicist Dr. Gerald Schroder. In his book, *The Science of God*, he shares mathematics that defy human logic: The "what if" scenario is literally thrown out the window. For example, he shares that another physicist, Professor Steven Weinberg, a noted Nobel laureate, calculates that the energy from the Big Bang is 10^{120}; if his calculation deviated by even one, in either direction, we would not be here, and this book would not have been written. That 120 figure is unique, because we recall that Genesis 6:3 says: "And the LORD said: 'My spirit shall not abide in man forever, for that he also is flesh; therefore, shall his days be a hundred and twenty years.'" Moses is the first character in the Bible who comes to embody this genetic DNA that is possessed by all of us within our telomeres. Mere coincidence, perhaps; by why didn't Moses live to be 118 years, or 100, or 125 years, instead of 120? It took scientists almost 3,500 years to discover and unravel the genetic time clock of human beings and all other species.

Are we going to perhaps live longer, like many of our predecessors in the Bible? Will this current generation witness the next wave of scientific breakthroughs? Does the Bible hold secrets not yet deciphered that can show us the future? If the above numbers aren't enough to warrant a belief in non-spontaneous mutation, then we are all just made up of carbon; but in order for carbon to form, according to Dr. Schroder, radioactive beryllium, with a mean life of 10 to the minus 16 seconds, must absorb the nucleus of helium that is .0000000000000001 seconds; if it can't find it in that length of time, we would not exist. And, no, this book could not have been written.

So, how do we get a glimpse of God playing God? In the Book of Psalms 90:4, we find: "A thousand years in Your sight are a day that passes in the night." If the universe is 15 billion years old and constantly expanding as Einstein demonstrated, then there are only three things that will remain constant in the universe: the speed of light at 186,000 miles per second in a vacuum; increased taxes by governments in power; and death, although the third can be prolonged by nutrition, decrease in stress, and modern-day science, which will transform human existence if given a chance.

Is it possible that we will visit other life forms in outer space? Is it possible that we are evolving by design and are separated by water and light-years in order for our species and others to not be self-destructive and to honor the basic ethos of the Two Tablets? Plate tectonics created Pangaea, the supercontinent that connected all seven continents into one landmass that started to separate about 200 million years ago; on September 12, 2013, Voyager became the first manmade object ever to leave our solar system after having been launched 36 years earlier on September 5, 1977. It is still traveling at approximately 38,000 miles per hour; and at that speed, it will take 17,500 years to reach one light year away. One light year is six trillion miles away. The closest known star, with the exception of our own sun, is Alpha Centauri, at 4.2 light-years away, and it is not known to have any planets.

The point is that it is possible that the Creator of the Universe kept all living intellectual life separated by geography, time limitations, and other obstacles to allow us to evolve into beings we were created to be, in the image of God. If life individually and collectively has any purpose, it is to propel us forward, to unravel that which is raveled. Dr. Viktor Frankl, a psychiatrist who witnessed the horrors of Auschwitz that he detailed in his bestselling book, *Man's Search for Meaning* (as we previously mentioned in the section titled "Work: Boredom or Satisfaction? Ecclesiastes" in Chapter 7) realized that our daily survival depends on having a purpose in life.

Take Two Tablets is not a means to end, but a means to a beginning. To live life a little better, a little healthier, a little longer for each of us serves, a purpose individually and collectively. The state of anarchy and chaos in our world that we experience along with the other 15,000 stimuli that affect us each day, block out what is in the essence in all our DNA in the nucleus of our being: to not just live but to achieve a higher existence, which gets us closer to whatever we are supposed to become, namely, to be more than what we are today in order to get to tomorrow.

You are probably wondering what is being suggested. Does following the basic tenets found in the Bible to the best of our ability advance us technologically? Do we win the prize by reaching the stars and by answering questions that we can just fathom today, like a cow in a pasture might ruminate about some obscure tractor? Without stability in the home and in our cities and in our world, we are doomed to never get past point A. With advancements in stem cell research, cloning organs, bioengineering, biorobots, advancements in cryo-medical sciences (freezing the body), and other unimaginable achievements, we will witness space travel, and the human race will survive. If collectively we fail, we don't survive. It seems that so much is not said in the Bible and is left to our imagination. If the message in II Kings 2:11–12 doesn't open up your imagination, what would? "Behold, there appeared a chariot of fire, and horses of fire, and parted them both asunder; and Elijah went up by a whirlwind into heaven. And Elisha saw it, and cried My father, my father, the chariot of Israel, and the horsemen thereof. And he saw him no more: and he took hold of his own clothes, and rent them in two pieces."

For years, scholars and Trekkies (those who are fascinated with Star Trek) have studied and discussed these verses. In short, there is no contradiction whatsoever in the Bible about whether there is intelligent life on other planets. In fact, to the contrary, sages would argue who would put a faucet on God's creativity. Now if that is our basic premise, why would it take a 100,000 years for humans to reach the closest star (excluding our sun), and millions of years to reach the billions of other stars and galaxies? We would wonder why it would take a hundred-plus million years for the continents to drift and separate, and what would eventually evolve into mankind, giving us enough of a separation from one another to attempt survival and existence.

Whether you believe that God, or some other intelligent energy force, or some spontaneous mutations created all that we are,
they all knew to not just separate mankind by oceans but to separate all intelligent life forces by light-years in order for us to evolve.

Recently, a new study in the Proceedings of the National Academy of Sciences shared that roughly 1 in 5 stars is similar to our
own sun, and might have a planet orbiting around it that is similar
to Earth's orbit of the sun. That adds up to more or less 40 billion
planets in our galaxy alone that may be similar to our planet: We
are not mathematicians, but we will take the odds that somewhere
out there some intelligent species are wondering exactly what we
are wondering.

As we shared earlier, it is in no way a contradiction to the Bible
to say that there is other intelligent life throughout the universe;
in fact, the Torah, Talmud, and such religious giants as Rambam
and the Lubavitcher Rebbe, Rabbi Menachem Mendel Schneerson,
make indirect or direct references to the possibility, saying that inasmuch as the Creator can create anything, why couldn't there be
intelligent life elsewhere in this vast universe of ours?

When Albert Einstein was asked if there was life on other
planets, he retorted, "Intelligent life on other planets? I'm not even
sure there is on earth!" Rod Serling, creator and executive produc-
er of the original *Twilight Zone* TV Series, became famous for his
trademark opening lines over the five years the show aired. In the
initial seasons, he opened with: "There is a fifth dimension, beyond
that which is known to man. It is a dimension as vast as space and
as timeless as infinity. It is the middle ground between light and
shadow, between science and superstition, and it lies between the
pit of man's fears and the summit of his knowledge. This is the
dimension of imagination. It is an area which we call the Twilight
Zone." Next came: "You're traveling through another dimension,
a dimension not only of sight and sound but of mind; a journey
into a wondrous land whose boundaries are that of imagination.
That's the signpost up ahead—your next stop, the Twilight Zone."
Finally, in the fourth season, he said: "You unlock this door with

the key of imagination. Beyond it is another dimension: a dimension of sound, a dimension of sight, a dimension of mind. You're moving into a land of both shadow and substance, of things and ideas; you've just crossed over into the Twilight Zone." (Living in America, staying up to 11 p.m. to watch reruns of the Twilight Zone was a rite of passage for many teenagers.)

A passage written a couple of thousands of years earlier in Ezekiel 1:1-28 reads: " . . . And I looked, and, behold, a stormy wind came out of the north, a great cloud, with a fire flashing up, so that a brightness was round about it; and out of the midst as the color of electrum, out of the midst of the fire. And out of the midst came the likeness of four living creatures. And this was their appearance: they had the likeness of a man . . . and they sparkled like the color of burnished brass. And they had the hands of a man under their wings on their four sides; and as for the faces and wings of them, four. Their wings were joined one to another; they turned not when they went; they went every one straight forward; it flashed up and down among the living creatures; and there was brightness to the fire, and out of the fire went forth lightning . . ." And in Jeremiah 4:13, it says: "Behold, he shall come up as clouds, and his chariots shall be as a whirlwind: his horses are swifter than eagles."

We will leave it up to the reader to interpret and decipher, for each of your answers is no more right or wrong than ours or those of any expert. It was forbidden to eat from the "Tree of Knowledge," but there were no directives that said we cannot learn from, share, and spread that knowledge, propelling us with futuristic technology, extended longevity, and unbounded imagination to seek and find other intelligence that might bring meaning to mankind's existence.

The authors of *Take Two Tablets* do not express belief one way or the other on what we have shared, except for the reality of what we are suggesting: that there has to be a purpose for all that is mentioned in the Bible and the lessons therein. Dr. Schroder also shares in his book, *The Science of God,* that respect of a stranger is mentioned 36 times in the entire Torah, more often than discussing observing the Sabbath. If we ultimately find ways of living beyond our allotted 120 years, the potential to visit other intellectual beings in the expanding universe will be that much greater, even though, individually, we are just participants for a mere blink of the eye.

We guess the Bible was given 3,500 years ago as the basic code of ethics for us to interpret, and its teachings apply as well today and tomorrow. As Charles Darwin so eloquently expressed in his *Origin of Species* (1859): "It is not the strongest of the species that survives, nor the most intelligent, but the one most responsive to change." In other words, we must adapt to the current environment in order to survive, yet hold on to the individual DNA that makes our social fabric so different from yet so similar to all our ancestors. It does not matter whether we are descended from Eve or from the seven daughters of Eve, who are the source of the entire inherent DNA from Mitochondrial Eve (as proposed by author Bryan Sykes).

The Hebrew word for the world is *olam*, which also means "eternal" and even "hidden"; God tells Moses, "This is My name le-olam" (forever hidden). We were left a code to interpret; however, the interpretation is not the important goal; more important is what we do with this newfound knowledge.

Have an amazing journey today and tomorrow and into the future, and try and find your purpose through it all.

About the Authors

Dr. Shmuel Einav, Emeritus Incumbent of the Herbert Berman Chair of Vascular Bioengineering of Tel Aviv University, is a world-distinguished expert in the field of biomedical engineering. Professor Einav won the prestigious 2012 Landau Prize for Scientific Research. Best known for his research in the field of coronary circulation, blood flow through blood vessels and heart valves, and blood-tissue interaction, he has published more than 130 articles, reviews, and abstracts. He is a Founding Fellow of the International Federation for Medical and Biological Engineering, a Founding Fellow of the Biomedical Engineering Society, a Fellow of the European Alliance for Medical and Biological Engineering & Science, and a Fellow of the American Federation for Medical and Biological Engineering. Dr. Einav is also a Fellow of the American Society of Mechanical Engineers, a Distinguished Scholar in Residence at Caltech, and Distinguished Research Professor and Director at Stony Brook University in New York. He is a founding member of the Tel Aviv and Los Angeles partnership and is the chair of the Technological Education committee of the Ministry of Education in Israel. He is married and is the father of three daughters and the proud grandfather of three grandchildren.

Dr. Peter Kash is the author of the international bestselling books *Make Your Own Luck, Restart: Life Tactics for Today's Economy* and *Freedom from Disease.* Together they were translated into eight languages and sold in more than 30 countries worldwide. Dr. Kash has been a biotech venture capitalist for over 25 years. He has helped to co-found a dozen biotech companies that have produced more than a half a dozen FDA-approved indications for several drugs, helping thousands of people worldwide. He earned a Doctorate in Education from Yeshiva University, an MBA in Finance from Pace University, and a B.S. in Management Science from SUNY Binghamton. He has been a Professor of Entrepreneurship and Marketing for more than 20 years and has taught at such prestigious institutions as the Wharton School of Business, University of Pennsylvania; Nihon University, (Japan); Hebrew University, (Israel); and the Polytechnic University (New York), and has served as a guest speaker at Ball State University, MIT/Harvard graduate school, Princeton University, Monash University (Australia). He is married and has four children.

Dr. Linda Friedland is an international health expert, medical doctor, television personality, well-regarded international speaker, and a bestselling author of five books. She is an authority on corporate health and well-being as well as women's health, stress management, parenting, and lifestyle interventions. She is one of the highest rated international speakers for many global organizations including many of the Fortune 500, and has spoken in more than 30 countries in the past few years. With a background of 20 years in clinical medicine combined with strategy expertise, Friedland consults internationally to healthcare, corporate, and financial institutions. She has developed and implemented numerous health, lifestyle, and illness-prevention programs for corporations through Asia, USA, Australia, Africa, and the UK. She is also a Graduate of the Australian Institute of Company Directors (GAICD) and a non-executive director. Dr. Friedland, who is based in Australia, is married, and is the mother of five children and grandmother of two boys.

CPSIA information can be obtained
at www.ICGtesting.com
Printed in the USA
FFOW05n1700100716

9 781887 043229